THE PLAYLIST
CHORD SONGBOOK

CW00660656

Published by
Wise Publications
14-15 Berners Street,
London, W1T 3LJ, UK.

Exclusive distributors:
Music Sales Limited,
Distribution Centre, Newmarket Road,
Bury St Edmunds, Suffolk,
IP33 3YB, UK.
Music Sales Pty Limited
120 Rothschild Avenue, Rosebery,
NSW 2018, Australia.

Order No. AM990385
ISBN 978-1-84772-063-4

This publication is not authorised for sale in the United States of America and / or Canada

Compiled by Nick Crispin.
Arranged by Matt Cowe.
Music processed by Paul Ewers Music Design.
Edited by Tom Farncombe.
Printed in the EU.

WISE PUBLICATIONS
part of The Music Sales Group
London / New York / Paris / Sydney / Copenhagen / Berlin / Madrid / Tokyo

www.musicsales.com

Anything Can Happen
In The Next Half Hour...

Words & Music by
Chris Batten, Roughton Reynolds, Liam Clewlow & Robert Rolfe

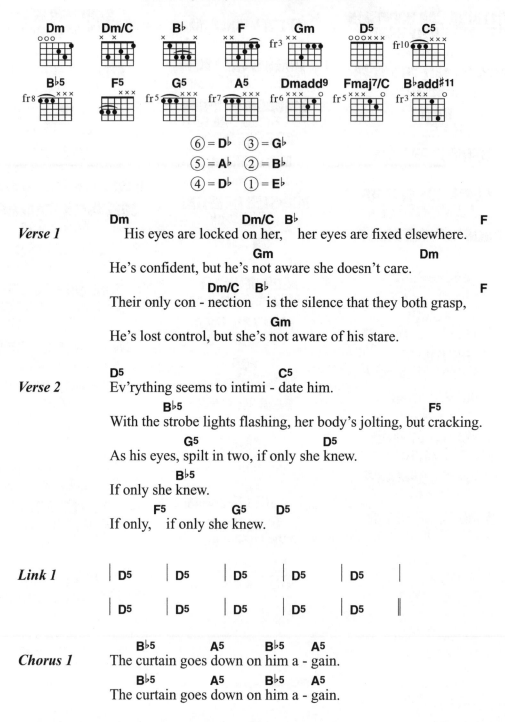

Verse 1

Dm   Dm/C   B♭   F
His eyes are locked on her,   her eyes are fixed elsewhere.

                     Gm   Dm
He's confident, but he's not aware she doesn't care.

                 Dm/C   B♭   F
Their only con - nection   is the silence that they both grasp,

                     Gm
He's lost control, but she's not aware of his stare.

Verse 2

D5   C5
Ev'rything seems to intimi - date him.

           B♭5   F5
With the strobe lights flashing, her body's jolting, but cracking.

                G5   D5
As his eyes, spilt in two, if only she knew.

             B♭5
If only she knew.

          F5   G5   D5
If only,   if only she knew.

Link 1

| D5 | D5 | D5 | D5 | D5 | |

| D5 | D5 | D5 | D5 | D5 | |

Chorus 1

         B♭5   A5   B♭5   A5
The curtain goes down on him a - gain.

         B♭5   A5   B♭5   A5
The curtain goes down on him a - gain.

Link 2 | N.C. (D5) | N.C. (D5) | N.C. (D5) | N.C. (D5) ‖

Verse 3
D5   C5
Ev'rything seems to be closing in on her,
   B♭5
It feels just like she is being hunted.
     F5
But it's all right, it's all good,
   G5   D5   B♭5 F5 G5
She's not aware, of his stare.

Bridge | Dmadd9 | Fmaj7/C | B♭add#11 | B♭add#11 ‖
     Dmadd9   Fmaj7/C   B♭add#11
We've had this   date from the be - ginning.
     Dmadd9   Fmaj7/C   B♭add#11   Dm Dm/C
We've had this   date from the be - ginning.

Chorus 2
   B♭5   A5   B♭5   A5
The curtain goes down on him a - gain.
   B♭5   A5   B♭5   A5
The curtain goes down on him a - gain.

Outro
B♭5   D5
Who remains when the cur - tain falls,
B♭5   C5
Remains when the curtain goes down?
B♭5   D5
Who remains when the cur - tain falls,
B♭5   C5   B♭5
Remains when the curtain goes down?

| N.C. (D5) | N.C. (D5) | N.C. (D5) | N.C. (D5) | Dm   ‖

Bones

Words & Music by
Brandon Flowers, Dave Keuning, Mark Stoermer & Ronnie Vannucci

Amaj⁷   Bm   F♯m   E   Dmaj⁷   C♯m   D   G♯5   C♯/E♯   B/D♯   A   C♯

Intro

N.C.
Come with me.

| **Amaj⁷** | **Amaj⁷** | **Bm** | **F♯m E** |

| **Dmaj⁷** | **Dmaj⁷** | **E** | **E** ||

(We took a)

Verse 1

    E   **C♯m**   **D**
We took a back road, we're gonna look at the stars,
         Bm   **C♯m**
We took a backroad in my car.
        F♯m   **D**
Down to the ocean, it's only water and sand,
        G♯5   **C♯m**
And in the ocean we'll hold hands.

Verse 2

    C♯m   **D**   **Bm**
But I don't really like you, apolo - getically dressed in the best,
         C♯m
But on a heartbeat glide.
      F♯m   **D**
Without an answer, the thunder speaks for the sky,
     G♯5   **C♯m** **D**
And on the cold, wet dirt I cry._____
       C♯m Bm A G♯5 F♯m   **E**
And on the cold, wet dirt I   cry.

Chorus 1

   (E)   **Amaj⁷**
Don't you wanna come with me?
             Bm   **F♯m E** **Dmaj⁷**
Don't you wanna feel my bones on your bones?
      E
It's only natural.

Verse 3

   E   **C♯m**   **D** **Bm**   **E**   **C♯/E♯**
A cinematic vision en - sued   like the holiest dream.
          F♯m
It's someone's calling?

```
             D
An angel whispers my name,
        G#5                      C#m    D
but the message relayed is the same:
                         E
"Wait till tomorrow, you'll be fine."

But it's gone to the dogs in my mind.
  C#m   D        Bm      C#m   F#m
I always hear them when the dead of night
        D        G#5   C#m    D
Comes calling to save me from this fight.
        C#m Bm  A     G#5 F#m      E
But they can ne - ver  wrong this  right.
```

Chorus 2
```
     (E)            Amaj7
Don't you wanna come with me?
                Bm    F#m E  Dmaj7
Don't you wanna feel my bones on your bones?
           E
It's only natural.
                Amaj7
Don't you wanna swim with me?
                Bm    F#m E   Dmaj7
Don't you wanna feel my skin    on your skin?
           E
It's only natural.
```

Bridge
```
     F#m                    C#/E#
(Never had a lover), I never had a lover.
     E               B/D#
(Never had soul), I never had soul.
     A                      C#
(Never had a good time), and I never had a good time.
     D             E
(Never got gold), I never got gold.
```

Chorus 3   As Chorus 2

Chorus 4
```
     E          A       D
Don't you wanna come with me?
                E    F#m E  Dmaj7
Don't you wanna feel my bones on your bones?
           E
It's only natural.
              A          D
Come and take a swim with me.
                E    F#m E   Dmaj7
Don't you wanna feel my skin    on your skin?
           E      A
It's only natural.
```

Bring It On Back

Words & Music by
Chris Cester & Nicholas Cester

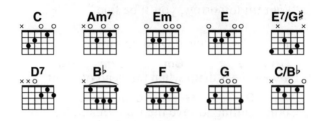

Verse 1

 C Am⁷   Em C
 Is it OK if I don't make it?

  Am⁷   Em   E
Is it OK if I don't come around?

    E⁷/G♯   Am⁷
The light is fading and the sun has gone down,

B♭   F   C
Bring it on back, bring it on back, bring it on back.

Verse 2

 C   Am⁷   Em C
 Where's the day that never ended?

  Am⁷   Em   E
Tell me when it's time to open up my eyes.

   E⁷/G♯   Am⁷   D⁷
Light the morning with the sun on the rise,

B♭   F   C
Bring it on back, bring it on back, bring it on back.

B♭   F   G
Bring it on back, bring it on back, bring it on back.

Chorus 1

   C   C/B♭
For all that you do, for all that you had,

 F   C
For all that you said, would you take it all back?

           C/B♭
When all that you see is much more than you have,

   F   B♭   C
I will bring it on back, bring it on back, bring it on back.

Verse 3

        C   Am⁷   Em   C

You won't know me till you need me,

              Am⁷   Em   E

But I won't let you down, so open up your eyes.

              E⁷/G♯   Am⁷   D⁷

The day is done the sun has set in the sky.

B♭   F   C

Bring it on back, bring it on back, bring it on back.

B♭   F   G

Bring it on back, bring it on back, bring it on back.

Chorus 2

          C   C/B♭

For all that you do, for all that you had,

       F   C

For all that you said, would you take it all back?

                       C/B♭

When all that you see is much more than you have,

       F   B♭   C

I will bring it on back, bring it on back, bring it on back.

        B♭   F   G

I'll bring it on back, bring it on back, bring it on back.

Bridge

B♭   F   C

   Just because your eyes are open doesn't mean that you see.

B♭   F   G

   So where do we go? Well, that's between you and me.

Interlude | C | C/B♭ | F | C   ‖

Chorus 3

        C   C/B♭

All that you do, for all that you had,

       F   C

For all that you said, would you take it all back?

                       C/B♭

When all that you see is much more than you have,

       F   B♭   C

I will bring it on back, bring it on back, bring it on back.

        B♭   F   C

I'll bring it on back, bring it on back, bring it on back.

        B♭   F   C

I'll bring it on back, bring it on back, bring it on back.

Broken Boy Soldier

Words & Music by
Brendan Benson & Jack White

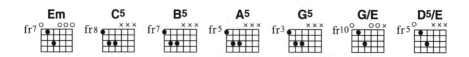

Intro

N.C.
| (Em) | (Em) | (Em) | (Em) | (Em) |

| (Em) | (Em) | (Em) | C5 B5 | A5 G5 ‖

‖: Em G/E Em | D5/E Em | Em G/E Em | D5/E Em :‖

Verse 1

Em G/E Em D5/E Em
  Well I'm pulling down ques - tions from the shelf,
  G/E Em D5/E Em
I'm asking for - give - ness.
     G/E Em D5/E Em
Oh, I ain't asking no - body but myself,
   G/E   Em D5/E Em C5 B5 A5 G5 Em
And I want you to know this,
   G/E   Em D5/E Em C5 B5 A5 G5 Em
And I want you to know this.

Verse 2

Em G/E Em D5/E Em   G/E Em D5/E Em
You're ri - fling through a box of toys that were handed down to me.
  G/E Em D5/E   Em
Just take out the ones you broke and then
   G/E Em D5/E Em
Give the rest to my fami - ly.
   G/E Em D5/E Em   G/E   Em D5/E Em
I'm gonna go back to school today, but I'm dropping my - self off.
  G/E   Em D5/E   Em
I'm throwing the childhood seat away,
    G/E Em D5/E Em C5 B5 A5 G5 Em
I'm through ripping my - self off,
     G/E Em D5/E Em C5 B5 A5 G5
I'm done ripping my - self off.

Chorus 1

Em   G/E Em D^5/E   Em
Well I'm child and man and   child again,

        G/E   Em D^5/E Em
A toy broken boy sold - ier.

       G/E Em D^5/E   Em
I'm child and man then   child again,

         G/E   Em D^5/E Em
The boy never gets old - er.

Bridge

N.C. (Em)
The boy never gets older.

The boy never gets older.

The boy never gets older.

                               C^5 B^5 A^5
The boy never gets older.

G^5 Em   G/E Em E^5/E Em
Never gets older.

Em   G/E   Em D^5/E Em   G/E Em D^5/E Em
The boy broken toy sold - ier.

Em   G/E Em D^5/E Em
The boy.

              C^5 B^5 A^5 G^5
The boy!

Outro

‖: Em | Em | Em | Em :‖ *Play 4 times*

Before I Fall To Pieces

Words & Music by
Johnny Borrell & Andy Burrows

Em¹¹   G   C   D   Dsus⁴   Dsus²   Am   Em

Capo seventh fret

Intro | Em¹¹   ‖: G   C | D Dsus⁴ D Dsus² :‖ *Play 6 times*
                                            (6°) Oh——

Verse 1
       G   C   D
(Oh,) one more drink and then I'll go,
          G   C   D
But there's one more thing I've got to know.
          G   C   D
Does he take you places that I don't?
             G   C   D
And what happened to the story that we wrote?

Pre-chorus 1
(D)   G   C   D   Dsus⁴
You just say you don't know,   you don't know.
D   Dsus² G   C   D
Oh no you don't know,   you don't know.

Link 1 | G   C | D Dsus⁴ D Dsus² | G   C | D Dsus⁴ D Dsus² ‖
                                                                    Oh,——

Verse 2
       G   C   D
(Oh,) let's just get this whole thing straight,
                        G   C   D
I don't want to kid - nap the truth then ne - gotiate.
       G   C   D
Or miss the point and aim at you,
             G   C   D
I just want to hear you say something that you be - lieve to be true.

Pre-chorus 2
```
(D)              G           C           D
But you say you don't know, you don't know.
                      G         C           D
You just say    you don't know,   you don't know
           G          C  D  Dsus4  D
What it feels like,——————————
Dsus2  G          C  D  Dsus4  D
What it feels like.——————————
```

Chorus 1
```
D    Dsus4    G
And so I'll go,
           C           D  Dsus4   D
Before I fall to pie - ces.
Dsus2      G
Yes I'll go,
           C           D  Dsus4
Before I fall to pie - ces.
```

Bridge 1
```
D    Dsus2  Am         D                  G     C
Now I'm just waiting for something that might never come.
       Am       D              G      C
If it's a million to one shot, I'll make sure I'm one.
             Em       D              G           C
Seems that nothing is certain except that truth turns to lies.
           G        C    G         D
Never figured it out or found out why.
```

Pre-chorus 3
```
                 G   C
And so I'll go,
           D
Yes I'll go.
           G   C
Yes I'll go,
           D
Yes I'll go,
                 G
Oh baby I'll go,
         C              D
Oh,—— yes I'll go.
           G
Yes I'll go,
C          D
Ah yes I'll go.
```

11

Chorus 2

G   C   D Dsus4 D Dsus2
Before I fall to pie - ces,

G   C   D Dsus4 D
Before I fall to pie - ces.

Dsus2   G
Yes I'll go,

         C   D Dsus4 D
Before I fall to pie - ces.

Dsus2   G
Yes I'll go,

         C   D Dsus4 D G C D
Before I fall to pie - ces.

Dsus4 D Dsus2 G   C   D
Oh,_____ oh,___ oh.___

Dsus4 D Dsus2 G   C   D
Oh,_____ oh,___ oh.___

Dsus4 D Dsus2 G   C   D Dsus4 D Dsus2
Oh,_____ oh,___ oh.___

Outro

G	C	D		G	C	D	

| G | C | G | D | G C | C | Em | D |

Calm Down Dearest

Words & Music by
Jamie Treays

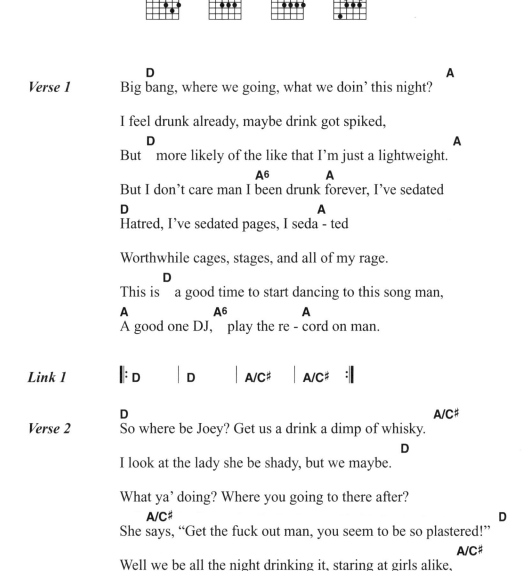

Verse 1

    D   **A**

Big bang, where we going, what we doin' this night?

I feel drunk already, maybe drink got spiked,

       D   **A**

But   more likely of the like that I'm just a lightweight.

                        A6   **A**

But I don't care man I been drunk forever, I've sedated

D   **A**

Hatred, I've sedated pages, I seda - ted

Worthwhile cages, stages, and all of my rage.

             D

This is   a good time to start dancing to this song man,

A   **A6**   **A**

A good one DJ,   play the re - cord on man.

Link 1   ‖: **D** | **D** | **A/C#** | **A/C#** :‖

Verse 2

D   **A/C#**

So where be Joey? Get us a drink a dimp of whisky.

                                          D

I look at the lady she be shady, but we maybe.

What ya' doing? Where you going to there after?

        A/C#   **D**

She says, "Get the fuck out man, you seem to be so plastered!"

                                        A/C#

Well we be all the night drinking it, staring at girls alike,

                                 D

It's all good man what goes on drink your can.

cont.

(D)
Walking it drunk down the Strand,
        A/C♯
And talk about how you missed the whole club queue.
        D
Well who the fuck are you?

Chorus 1

       A/C♯
It's heavy, it's on my mind,
           D
'Cause you say that you feel just   fine.
          A
(He's) racking and stacking them lines,
       D
I said calm down dearest.
       A/C♯
It's heavy, it's on my mind,
         D
'Cause you say that you feel just   fine.
         A
(You're) racking and stacking your lines,

I say calm down dearest.

Verse 3

    D   **N.C.**
I re - member shooting shit down the old alleyways,

Talking tragedies of music like old Holiday.

I remember what we doing then, I don't remember now.
              D
It's the past it's the future, I don't know how to carry on

Through the rights and wrongs and kick it like we know the songs,
 A/C♯   **D**
Al - ready before we rock steady down and on the dancefloor.

And I don't get no fights, when I get angry drunk,
 A/C♯
I sit down in the corner and sulk my fucking socks off.

Verse 4

    D   **A/C♯**
So who the fuck are we? Just the boys in the city,

                                           D
It's all been done before and we do it again so.

                               A/C♯
We'll see you later you alligators,

                                                           D
We'll be back I'm sure next week and sit in the bar you know.

                                    A/C♯
So bye, bye, bye we'll try never to die but,

                                             D
We are so young, we don't understand if we canna fly.

                                    A/C♯
So we're here now, we will be gone soon,

                                           D
But not today, not tomorrow, not in the next tune.

Chorus 2

       D   **A/C♯**
‖: It's heavy, it's on my mind,

                             D
'Cause you say that you feel just   fine.

                             A
(He's) racking and stacking them lines,

                   D
Say calm down dearest.

                  A/C♯
It's heavy, it's on my mind,

                        D
You say that you feel just   fine.

                              A
(You're) racking and stacking your lines,

                    D
I say calm down dearest.   :‖ *Repeat to fade*

15

Dashboard

Words & Music by
Isaac Brock, Jeremiah Green, Eric Judy, Johnny Marr, Tom Peloso & Joe Plummer

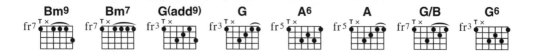

Intro | Bm⁹ Bm⁷ | Gadd⁹ G | A⁶ A | A⁶ A ‖

(Well, it)

Verse 1

  (A) G/B Bm⁷
Well, it would - 've been,

      G⁶ G   A⁶ A A⁶ A
Could've been worse than you would ever know.

  Bm⁹   Bm⁷
Oh, the dash - board melted,

  G(add⁹) G   A⁶ A A⁶ A
But we   still have the radio.

  Bm⁷   Bm⁷
Oh, it should - 've been,

     G(add⁹) G   A⁶ A A⁶ A
Could've been worse than you would ever know.

   G/B Bm⁷
Well, you told me about nowhere,

    G⁶ G   A⁶ A⁶ A A⁶ A
Well it sounds like someplace I'd like to go.

  Bm⁹   Bm⁷
Oh, it could - 've been,

     G(add⁹) G   A⁶   A A⁶ A
Should've been worse than you would ever know.

  Bm⁹   Bm⁷   G(add⁹) G
Well, the wind - shield was broken but I love the fresh air y'know.

A⁶ A   A⁶ A
 (The dashboard melted but we still have the radio.)

  Bm⁹   Bm⁷
Oh, it would - 've been,

     G(add⁹) G   A⁶
Could've been worse than you would ever know, oh!

cont.

      A   **A⁶** **A**
(The dashboard melted but we still have the radio.)

      Bm⁹   **Bm⁷**
Oh, we talked about nothing,

           G(add⁹) G   **A**
Which was more   than I wanted you to know, oh, oh, oh, oh.

Now here we go!

Link 1

| | **Bm⁷** | | **Bm⁷** | | |

‖: **Bm⁹** **B⁷** | **G(add⁹)** **G** | **A⁶** **A** | **A⁶** **A** :‖

| **Bm⁷** | | **G** | | **A** | |

Verse 2

N.C. G/B
Oh! It would've been,

                                       A⁶ A A⁶ A
Could've been worse than it had even gone.

      Bm⁹   **Bm⁷**   **G(add⁹)**
Well, the car was on blocks, but I was

G   **A⁶**
Already where I want.

A   **A⁶**   **A**
(It was impossible, we ran it good, we ran it good.)

      Bm⁷   **Bm⁷**   **G(add⁹) G**   **A⁶**
Why should we ever even ever really   even get to know?

A   **A⁶**   **A**
(It was impossible, we ran it good, we ran it good.)

         Bm⁹ **Bm⁷**   **G(add⁹)**
Oh if the world don't like us it'll shake us

G   **A⁶** **A**   **A⁶**   **A**
Just like we were a co - oh - oh - oh - old.

                   Bm⁷
Now here we go!

Bridge 1

       Bm7   **G**
Well we scheme and we scheme but we always blow it,

      A
We've yet to crash, but we still might as well enjoy it.

       Bm7   **G**
Standing at a light switch to each east and west horizon,

      A
Every dawn when you're surprising

And the evening was consoling.

       Bm7   **G**   **A**
Saying "See it wasn't quite as bad as."

Verse 3

      (Bm7)
Well, it would've been,

Could've been worse than you would ever know.

                  (Bm7/D)
I was patiently erasing and re - cording the wrong episodes.
(Bm7/E)
After you had proved my point wrong,

             (Bm7)   **(Bm7/D)**   **(Bm7/E)**
It wasn't like I'd let it go, oh, oh, oh. Oh, oh, oh.

     (Bm7)   **(Bm7/D)**   **Bm7**
I just wanted to catch the last laugh of this show.

Link 2

| **Bm9** **Bm7** | **G(add9)** **G**| **A6** **A** | **A6** **A** |

| **G/B** **Bm7** | **G6** **G** | **A6** **A** | **A6** **A** ‖

Verse 4

      Bm9   **Bm7**
Yeah, it would - 've been,

             G(add9) **G**   **A6** **A** **A6** **A**
Could've been worse   than you would ever know.

     G/B   **Bm7**   **G6** **G**   **A6**
Oh, the dash - board melted, but we still have the radio.

    A   **A6**   **A**
(The dashboard melted, but we ran it good, we ran it good.)
Bm9   **Bm7**   **G(add9)** **G**
Hard - wired to conceive, so much   we'd have to stow it,

    A6   **A**   **A6**
Even needs have needs, tiny giants made of tinier giants.
Bm9   **Bm7**   **G(add9)** **G**   **A6**
Don't wear eyelids so I don't   miss the last laugh of this show.

    A   **A6**   **A**
(The dashboard melted but we still have the radio.)

Verse 5

Bm⁹   **Bm⁷**
Oh, we could' - ve been,

            G(add⁹)   **G**   **A⁶**
Should've been worse   than you would ever know.

      A   **A⁶**   **A**
(The dashboard melted but we still have the radio)

Bm⁹ **Bm⁷**
Well, you told me about nowhere

        G(add⁹)   **G**   **A⁶**   **A**   **A⁶**
Well it sounds   like someplace I'd like to go, oh, oh, oh, oh.

A
Now here we go!

Bridge 2

           Bm⁷   **G**
Well we scheme and we scheme but we always blow it,

      A
We've yet to crash, but we still might as well enjoy it.

           Bm⁷   **G**
Standing at a light switch to each east and west horizon,

      A
Every dawn when you're surprising

And the evening was consoling.

          Bm⁷   **G**   **A**
Saying "See it wasn't quite as bad as."

        N.C.
Oh, it would've been,

        G   **N.C.**
Could've been worse than you would ever know.

Elusive

Words & Music by
Scott Matthews

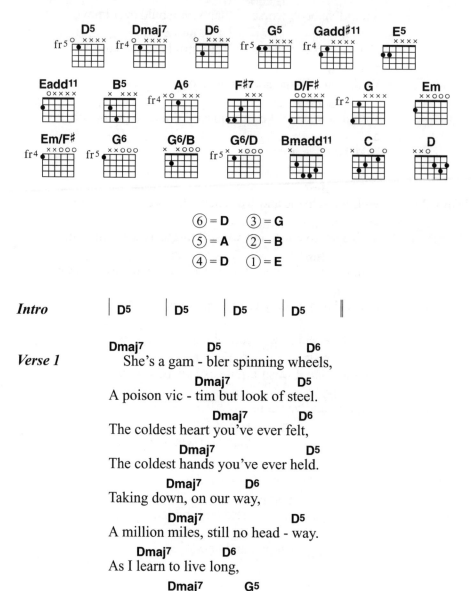

Intro | D5 | D5 | D5 | D5 ‖

Verse 1

Dmaj7   D5   D6
She's a gam - bler spinning wheels,

        Dmaj7   D5
A poison vic - tim but look of steel.

        Dmaj7   D6
The coldest heart you've ever felt,

        Dmaj7   D5
The coldest hands you've ever held.

     Dmaj7   D6
Taking down, on our way,

     Dmaj7   D5
A million miles, still no head - way.

    Dmaj7   D6
As I learn to live long,

     Dmaj7   G5
In a mind I'm proud to roam.

Chorus 1

G5   Gadd#11   E5
She's elu - sive and I'm a - wake,

              Eadd11   B5
You're finally real, there's nothing fake.

                    A6
A mystery now to me and you,

                        F#7
Open my eyes and I'm next to you.

   D/F#   G Gadd#11 G   D5
She said my desti - ny lies in the hands that set me free.

Verse 2

Dmaj7   D5   D6
   A reckless night, she hears me breathe,

           Dmaj7   D5
Cursing the sky at this compa - ny.

          Dmaj7   D6
They lost the wis - dom deep in - side,

          Dmaj7   D5
When bitter - ness shows its side.

       Dmaj7   D6
If it's true, I am doom - ed,

          Dmaj7   D5
What more is there to hold on to?

          Dmaj7   D6
A strand of her hair is all I own,

       Dmaj7   G5
A gift to me, this sorry soul.

Chorus 2

G5   Gadd#11   E5
She's elu - sive and I'm a - wake,

              Eadd11   B5
You're finally real, there's nothing fake.

                    A6
A mystery now to me and you,

                        F#7
Open my eyes and I'm next to you.

       D/F#   G   Gadd#11 G   (Em)
She said my desti - ny lies in the   hands that set me free.

Link 1

‖: Em   Em/F#   G6   G6/B   G6/D :‖ *Play 3 times*

| Em Em/F# G6 | D5 | D5 | ‖

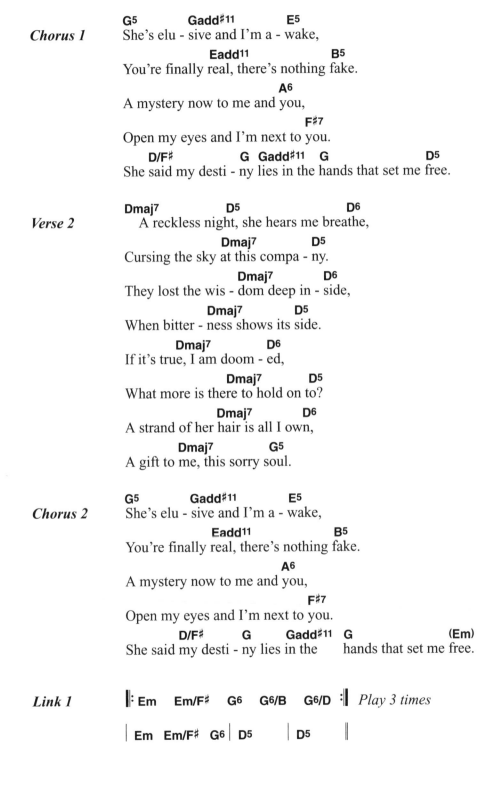

Verse 3

Dmaj7   D5   D6
The sun in sails, and this ain't right.

      Dmaj7   D5
There's more to her than meets the eye.

     Dmaj7   D6
She comes and goes at any time,

     Dmaj7   G5
Back in my head another time.

Chorus 3

G5
She's elusive and I'm a - wake,

           Em

             B5
You're finally real, there's nothing fake.

         A6
A mystery now to me and you,

           F#7
Open my eyes and I'm next to you.

        G   Bmadd11
She said my destiny lies in the hands that set me free.

Outro

Bmadd11 C D
Ooh,   ooh, ooh, ooh, ooh, ooh, ooh, ooh, ooh.——

Bmadd11 C D
Ooh,   ooh, ooh, ooh, ooh, ooh, ooh, ooh, ooh.——

Bmadd11 C D
Ooh,   ooh, ooh, ooh, ooh, ooh, ooh, ooh, ooh.——

Bmadd11 C
Ooh,   ooh.

‖: D5 | D5 | D5 | D5 :‖

Herculean

Words & Music by
Damon Albarn & Paul Simonon

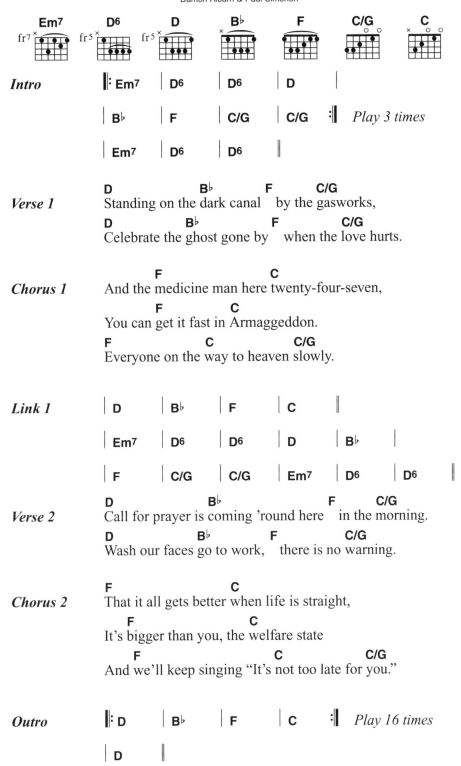

Intro

‖: Em7 | D6 | D6 | D |

| Bb | F | C/G | C/G :‖ *Play 3 times*

| Em7 | D6 | D6 ‖

Verse 1

D   Bb   F   C/G
Standing on the dark canal   by the gasworks,
D   Bb   F   C/G
Celebrate the ghost gone by   when the love hurts.

Chorus 1

             F   C
And the medicine man here twenty-four-seven,
            F   C
You can get it fast in Armaggeddon.
F   C   C/G
Everyone on the way to heaven slowly.

Link 1

| D | Bb | F | C ‖

| Em7 | D6 | D6 | D | Bb |

| F | C/G | C/G | Em7 | D6 | D6 ‖

Verse 2

D   Bb   F   C/G
Call for prayer is coming 'round here   in the morning.
D   Bb   F   C/G
Wash our faces go to work,   there is no warning.

Chorus 2

F   C
That it all gets better when life is straight,
     F   C
It's bigger than you, the welfare state
     F   C   C/G
And we'll keep singing "It's not too late for you."

Outro

‖: D | Bb | F | C :‖ *Play 16 times*

| D ‖

© Copyright 2007 Chrysalis Music Limited.
All Rights Reserved. International Copyright Secured.

23

Four Winds

Words & Music by
Conor Oberst

F#m   D   A   Bm   E

Capo 1st Fret

Intro

‖: F#m | D | A | Bm |

| A | Bm | D | D :‖ *Play 4 times*

Verse 1

F#m   D
Your class, your caste, your country, sect, your name or your tribe.
       A   Bm
There's people always dying, trying to keep them alive.
       A   Bm
There's bodies decomposing in con - tainers tonight,
           D
In an a - bandoned building where…
       F#m   D
A squatter's made a mural of a Mexican girl,
       A   Bm
With fifteen cans of spray paint in a chemical swirl.
       A   Bm
She's standing in the ashes at the end of the world,
              D
Four winds   blowing through her hair.

Chorus 1

(D)   Bm   E   Bm   E
But when great Satan's gone, the whore of Baby - lon,
           D   A   D   A
She just can't sus - tain the pressure where it's placed.
       Bm   E
She caves.

Link 1

| F#m | D | A | Bm |

| A | Bm | D | D ‖

Verse 2

       F#m   D
The Bible's blind, the Torah's deaf, the Qu'ran's mute.
       A   Bm
If you burn them all together you get close to the truth still,
       A   Bm
They're pouring over sanskrit on the ivy league moons,
              D
While shadows   lengthen in the sun.

| | D |
| *cont.* | While shadows   lengthen in the sun. |

                         F♯m   D
            Cast on a school and meditation built to soften the times,
                 A   Bm
            And hold us at the centre while the spiral unwinds.
                 A   Bm
            It's knocking over fences, crossing property lines,
                       D
            Four winds,   cry until it comes.

                    (D)   Bm   E
Chorus 2   And it's the son of man,
                                 Bm   E
            Slouching towards Bethle - hem.
                         D   A   D   A
            A heart just can't con - tain all of that empty space.
                 Bm   E
            It breaks, it breaks, it breaks.

Link 2 | F♯m | D | F♯m | A |

              | F♯m | D | E | E   ‖
                                      (Well I went)

                    (E)   F♯m   D
Verse 3   Well, I went back, I rent a Cadillac, a company jet,
                 A   Bm
            Like a newly orphaned refugee, re - tracing my steps.
                 A   Bm
            All the way to Casa David to com - mune with the dead.
                       D
            They said, "You'd better look alive."
                         F♯m   D
            And I was off to old Dakota where a genocide sleeps,
                 A   Bm
            In the black hills, the bad lands, the calloused east.
                 A   Bm
            I buried my ballast, I made my peace,
                             D
            With four winds   levelling the pines.

                         Bm   E   Bm   E
Chorus 3   But when great Satan's gone, the whore of Baby - lon,
                             D   A   D   A
            Well she just can't re - main with all that outer space.
                 Bm   E
            She breaks, she breaks,
                 Bm   E   F♯m
            She caves, she caves.

Golden Skans

Words & Music by
Jamie Reynolds, James Righton & Simon Taylor

Dm   C6   Gm   Am   C7   fr3

Intro

Dm   C6
Ooh,——— ah.

Gm   Am
Ooh,——— ah.

Dm   C6
Ooh,——— ah.

Gm   Am
Ooh,——— ah.

Chorus 1

Dm   C6   Gm
Light touched my hands in a dream of Golden Skans, from now on,

                    Am
You can for - get all future plans.

Dm   C6
Night touched my hands with the turning Golden Skans,

                    Gm   Am
From the night to the light, all plans are golden in your hands.

Verse 1

Dm   Am   Gm   Am
   Set sail from sense,   bring all her young.

Dm   Am   Gm
We sail from where we once be - gun.

                    Am
While we wait, while we wait.

Bridge 1

          Dm   C6
A hall of records, or numbers, or spaces still undone,

Gm   Am
Ruins, or relics, dis - ciples and the young.

          Dm   C6
A hall of records, or numbers, or spaces still undone,

Gm   Am
Ruins, or relics, dis - ciples and the young.

Chorus 2   As Chorus 1

Link 1
```
Dm    C7
Ooh,——— ah.
Gm    Am
Ooh,——— ah.
Dm    C7
Ooh,——— ah.
Gm    Am
Ooh,——— ah.
```

Verse 2
```
Dm                        Am              Gm    Am
    We sailed from sense,   brought all our young.
Dm              Am              Gm
We sailed from where we once be - gun.
            Am
While we wait, while we wait.
```

Bridge 2   As Bridge 1

Chorus 3   ‖: As Chorus 1 :‖

Outro
```
Dm    C7
Ooh,——— ah.
Gm    Am
Ooh,——— ah.
Dm    C7
Ooh,——— ah.
Gm    Am
Ooh,——— ah.

Dm
Ooh,——— ah.

Ooh,——— ah.

Ooh,——— ah.

Ooh,——— ah.
```

Gone Daddy Gone

Words & Music by
Willie Dixon & Gordon Gano

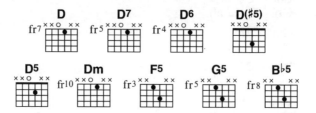

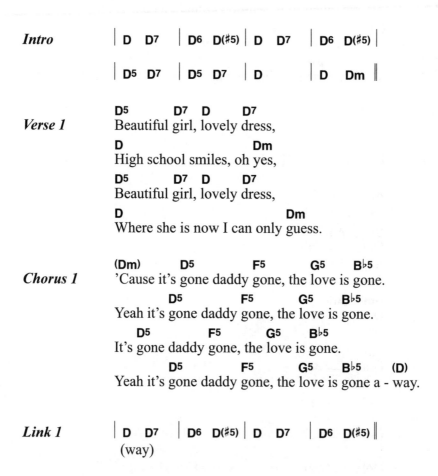

Intro | D D7 | D6 D(♯5) | D D7 | D6 D(♯5) |

| D5 D7 | D5 D7 | D | D Dm ‖

Verse 1

D5   D7 D   D7
Beautiful girl, lovely dress,

D   Dm
High school smiles, oh yes,

D5   D7 D   D7
Beautiful girl, lovely dress,

D   Dm
Where she is now I can only guess.

Chorus 1

(Dm)   D5   F5   G5   B♭5
'Cause it's gone daddy gone, the love is gone.

         D5   F5   G5   B♭5
Yeah it's gone daddy gone, the love is gone.

   D5   F5   G5   B♭5
It's gone daddy gone, the love is gone.

        D5   F5   G5   B♭5   (D)
Yeah it's gone daddy gone, the love is gone a - way.

Link 1 | D D7 | D6 D(♯5) | D D7 | D6 D(♯5) ‖
(way)

Verse 2

D5   D7 D D7
When I   see you,

D   Dm
Eyes will turn blue,

D5   D7 D D7
When I   see you,

  D   Dm
A thousand eyes turning blue.

Chorus 2

As Chorus 1

Interlude

‖: D D7 | D6 D(♯5) | D D7 | D6 D(♯5) :‖

Bridge

      D   D7   D6   D(♯5)
I can tell by the way that you switch and walk,

           D   D7   D6   D(♯5)
And I can see by the way that you   baby talk.

          D5   D7   D   D7
And I can know by the way that you treat your man.

      D   Dm
I can love you baby, till it's a crime.

Chorus 3

As Chorus 1

Verse 3

D5   D7 D   D7
Beautiful girl, lovely dress,

D   Dm
Fifteen smiles, oh yes.

D5   D7 D   D7
Beautiful girl, lovely dress.

D   Dm
Where she is now I can only guess.

Chorus 4

(Dm)   D5   F5   G5   B♭5
'Cause it's gone daddy gone, the love is gone.

           D5   F5   G5   B♭5
Yeah it's gone daddy gone, the love is gone.

     D5   F5   G5   B♭5
It's gone daddy gone, the love is gone.

          D5   F5   G5   B♭5   D   D7 D6
Yeah it's gone daddy gone, the love is gone a - way.

Outro

‖: D(♯5) D D7 D6 :‖ *Play 7 times*
Gone a - way.

Gravity's Rainbow

Words & Music by
Jamie Reynolds, James Righton & Simon Taylor

Intro

| N.C. (C) (Em/B) | (Em6) (E♭aug) |

| N.C. (C) (Em/B) | (Em6) (E♭aug) ‖

Verse 1

C   Em/B   Em6   E♭aug
Come on with me through ruined Lipglock,

C   Em/B   Em6   E♭aug
Across Tan - gian   deserts we'll flock.

C   Em/B   E♭aug
Madcap Me - dusa   Flank my Foghorn,

C   Em/B   Em6   E♭aug
We'll change four seasons with our first born.

Link 1

‖: C   Em/B | Em   D | C   Em/B | Em   D :‖

Verse 2

C   Em/B   Em6   E♭aug
All ships of sense on hyper ocean,

C   Em/B   Em6   E♭aug
All Kytes of chaos   still in motion.

C   Em/B   Em6   E♭aug
My culture vulture such a dab hand,

C   Em   Em6   E♭aug
I'll steal you from the year four thousand.

Chorus 1

```
          C            Em/B           Em
          Come with me, come with me,
                       B7/D♯   C
          We'll travel to infini - ty.
                       Em/B                Em
          Come with me, come with me,
                       B7/D♯      C
          We'll travel to infini - ty.
                 Em/B      Em      B7/D♯          C
          I'll always be there, uh, oh, my future love.
                 Em/B      Em      B7/D♯         (C)
          I'll always be there, for you, my future love.
```

Link 2

```
‖: C     Em/B    | (Em6)  (E♭aug) |
 | C     Em/B    | (Em6)  (E♭aug) :‖
```

Verse 3

```
          C                   Em/B   Em6      E♭aug
          Your tears leave trails of Tik - Volt - Lauf droom.
          C            Em/B   Em6  E♭aug
          Autono - ma, the rubix bloom groom.
          C                 Em/B    Em6    E♭aug
          Those crippled lines that I can't get to
          C                  Em/B    Em6    E♭aug
          You'd slip through time but I won't let you.
```

Chorus 2   As Chorus 1

Chorus 3

```
       C            Em/B           Em
‖: Come with me, come with me,
              D         C
   We'll travel to infini - ty.
           Em/B                Em
   Come with me, come with me,
              D         C
   We'll travel to infini - ty.
      Bm/B      Em       D          C
   I'll always be there, uh, oh, my future love.
      Em/B      Em       D          C
   I'll always be there, for you, my future love. :‖  Play 3 times
```

Hang Me Up To Dry

Words & Music by
Nathan Willett, Matthew Maust, Jonathan Russell & Matthew Aveiro

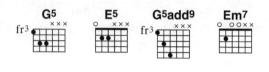

Intro | G5 | G5 | E5 | E5   ‖

Verse 1
G5
Careless in our summer clothes splashing
 E5
A - round in the muck and the mire.
G5
Careless in our summer clothes splashing
 E5
A - round in the muck and the mire.

| G5 | G5 | E5 | E5 |

G5   E5
Fell asleep with stains, cake deep in the knees, what a pain.

Chorus 1
  G5   E5
Now hang me up to dry, you wrung me out too,

Too, too many times.
  G5   E5
Now hang me up to dry, I'm pearly like the whites,

The whites of your eyes.

Link 1   ‖: G5add9 | G5add9 | Em7 | Em7   :‖

| G5 | G5 | E5 | E5 |

Verse 2
G5   E5
All mixed up in the wash, hot water bleeding our colours.
G5   E5
All mixed up in the wash, hot water bleeding our colours.

Chorus 2

        G5   **E5**

Now hang me up to dry, you wrung me out too,

Too, too many times.
        G5   **E5**

Now hang me up to dry, I'm pearly like the whites,

The whites of your eyes.

Link 2   ‖: **G5add9** | **G5add9** | **Em7** | **Em7** :‖

        | **G5** | **G5** | **E5** | **E5** |

Chorus 3

        G5   **E5**

Now hang me up to dry, you wrung me out too,

Too, too many times.
        G5   **E5**

Now hang me up to dry, I'm pearly like the whites,

The whites of your eyes.

Chorus 4

        N.C.

Now hang me up to dry, you wrung me out too, too, too many times.

Now hang me up to dry, I'm pearly like the whites, the whites of your eyes.

It Overtakes Me

Words & Music by
Wayne Coyne, Steven Drozd & Michael Ivins

E   B   C#m   G#m   A   C#sus2/G#   F#m

Intro ‖: E | E | E | A E :‖

Verse 1

N.C.
It overtakes me, it overtakes me, it overtakes me, oh, I.
C#m   G#m   A
It overtakes me, it master-slaves me, it overtakes me, oh.

Link 1 ‖: E | E | E | A E :‖

Verse 2

N.C.
It overtakes me, it overtakes me, it overtakes me, oh, I.
C#sus2/G#   G#m   A
It overtakes me, it wakes and bakes me, it overtakes me, oh.

Link 2 | C#m | C#m | C#m | G#m |

C#m   G#m
 You know that it isn't real.

| E | E | E | A E ‖

Bridge 1

C#m
 You know that it isn't real.
     G#m   C#m
You'll disap - pear in a black hole.

You know that it isn't real.
     G#m
Floating out of control.

Link 3

      E   A   E
It overtakes me, it overtakes me, it overtakes me, oh, I.

‖: F♯m   C♯m | C♯m | F♯m B | B   :‖ B   ‖

Verse 3

      E   A   E
It overtakes me, it overtakes me, it overtakes me, oh, I.
      E   A   E
It overtakes me, it master-slaves me, it overtakes me, oh.

Bridge 2

C♯m   G♯m C♯m
  You know that it isn't real.
                                G♯m
You know that it isn't real.

Verse 4

‖:   E   A   E
It overtakes me, it overtakes me, it overtakes me, oh, I.
    E   A   E
It overtakes me, it wakes and bakes me, it overtakes me, oh.   :‖

Joker & The Thief

Words & Music by
Andrew Stockdale, Chris Ross & Myles Heskett

D5　Csus2　F5　G5　D5*　F5*　G5*

(6) = D　(3) = G
(5) = A　(2) = B
(4) = D　(1) = E

Intro　‖: N.C. (D5) | N.C. (D5) | N.C. (D5) | N.C. (D5) :‖ *Play 3 times*

| D5 | D5 | Csus2 | Csus2 |

| D5 | D5 | Csus2 | Csus2 |

| F5 | F5 | G5 | G5 ‖

| D5* | D5* | D5* | D5* |

| D5* | D5* | F5* | F5* |

| D5* | D5* ‖

Verse 1

D5*
I said the joker is a wanted man,

He makes his way all across the land,

See him sifting through the sand.

F5*　　　　　　　　　　　　　G5*　　　　　　　　　　F5*
So I'll tell you all the story about the joker and the thief in the night.

Link 1　| D5* | D5* | D5* | D5* ‖

Pre-chorus 1

D5*
He's always laughing in the midst of power,

Always living in the final hour.

There is always sweet and sour,

F5*　G5*　　　(D5)
So we are not going home.

Link 2 | D5 | D5 | Csus2 | Csus2 ‖
        (home)

        D5   Csus2
Chorus 1   Can you see the joker flying over,

        D5   Csus2
        As she's standing in the field of clover?

        F5
        Watching out everyday,

         G5
        I wonder what would happen if he took her away?

        ‖: D5* | D5* | D5* | D5* :‖

        D5*
Verse 2   What you see well you might not know,

        You get the feelin' comin' after the glow,

        The vagabond is moving slow.

            F5*
        So I'll tell you all the story 'bout the
        G5*   (D5*)
        Joker and the thief in the night.

Link 3 | D5* | D5* | D5* | D5* ‖
        (night)

        D5*
Pre-chorus 2   All the people that you see in the night,

        Hold their dreams up to the light,

        Where the beast is searching for sight
            F5*   G5*   (D5)
        And we are not going home.

Link 4 | D5 | D5 | Csus2 | Csus2 ‖
        (home)

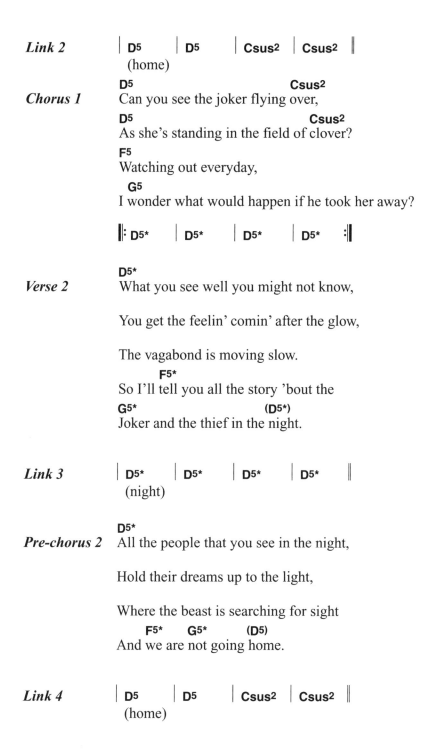

37

Chorus 2

D5   **Csus2**
Can you see the joker flying over,

D5   **Csus2**
As she's standing in the field of clover?

F5
Watching out everyday,

  G5
I wonder what would happen if he took her away?

Interlude

| ‖: D5 | D5 | Csus2 | Csus2 |
| D5 | D5 | Csus2 | Csus2 |
| F5 | F5 | G5 | G5 | :‖

half time feel

| D5 | D5 Csus2 | D5 |
| D5 Csus2 | D5 | D5 Csus2 |
| F5 | F5 | G5 | G5 | ‖

a tempo

| D5 | D5 | D5 | D5 | F5 |
| G5 | D5* | D5* | D5* | D5* | ‖

Verse 3

D5*
I said the joker is a wanted man,

He makes his way all across the land,

See him sifting through the sand.

    F5*
So I'll tell you all the story 'bout the

G5*
Joker and the thief,

      F5*
I said, I'll tell all you the story 'bout the

G5*
Joker and the thief,

      F5*
I said,   I'll tell the story 'bout the

G5*   **D5**
Joker and the thief in the night.

Monster Hospital

Words & Music by
James Shaw & Emily Haines

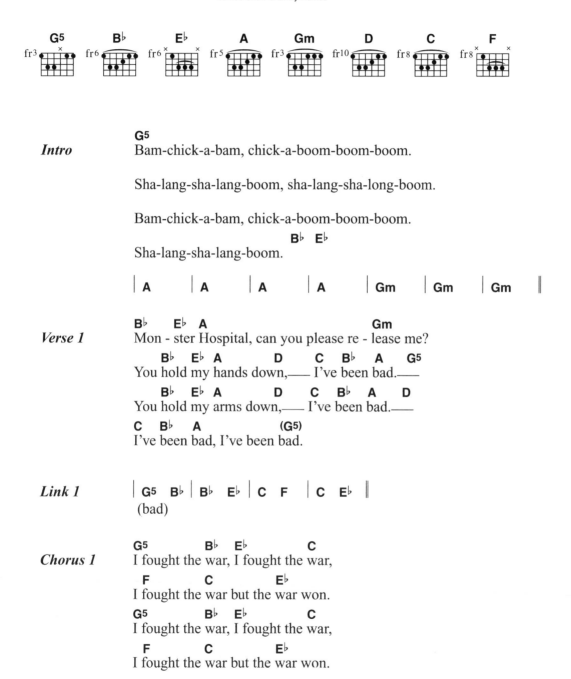

Intro

G5
Bam-chick-a-bam, chick-a-boom-boom-boom.

Sha-lang-sha-lang-boom, sha-lang-sha-long-boom.

Bam-chick-a-bam, chick-a-boom-boom-boom.

             B♭ E♭
Sha-lang-sha-lang-boom.

| A | A | A | A | Gm | Gm | Gm ‖

Verse 1

B♭   E♭ A   Gm
Mon - ster Hospital, can you please re - lease me?

    B♭ E♭ A   D   C B♭ A G5
You hold my hands down,___ I've been bad.___

    B♭ E♭ A   D   C B♭ A D
You hold my arms down,___ I've been bad.___

C B♭ A   (G5)
I've been bad, I've been bad.

Link 1

| G5 B♭ | B♭ E♭ | C F | C E♭ ‖
(bad)

Chorus 1

G5   B♭ E♭   C
I fought the war, I fought the war,

   F   C   E♭
I fought the war but the war won.

G5   B♭ E♭   C
I fought the war, I fought the war,

   F   C   E♭
I fought the war but the war won.

Link 2 | G5 | G5 | G5   ‖

              B♭   E♭ A   Gm

Verse 2   Mon - ster Movie, Daddy Warbucks up against Bobby Fuller,

                  B♭   E♭ A   D

And he beat him hands down.——

           C   B♭   A   D

Lead in his head,——

                          C B♭ A   G5

They put a little lead in,   in his head.

Link 3 | G5 B♭ | B♭ E♭ | C F | C E♭ ‖
                (head)

            G5   B♭ E♭   C

Chorus 2   I fought the war, I fought the war,

            F   C   E♭

I fought the war but the war won.

            G5   B♭ E♭   C F   C

I fought the war, I fought the war, I fought the war

                  E♭   G5   B♭

But the war won't stop for the love of God.

           E♭   C F   C   E♭

I fought the war, I fought the war but the war won.

Interlude   ‖: G5 | G5 | G5 | G5 |

             | A | A | A | A   :‖

           N.C.

Chorus 3   I fought the war, I fought the war, I fought the war

But the war won't stop for the love of God.

I fought the war, I fought the war

                        G5   B♭

But the war won't stop for the love of God.

           E♭   C F   C

I fought the war, I fought the war,

                  E♭   G5   B♭

But the war won't stop for the love of God.

           E♭   C F   C   E♭

I fought the war, I fought the war but the war won.

Link 4 ｜ **G5 B♭** ｜ **B♭ E♭** ｜ **C F** ｜ **C E♭** ‖

Chorus 4

G5   **B♭ E♭**   **C   F**   **C**
I fought the war, I fought the war, I fought the war
          E♭   **G5**   **B♭**
But the war won't stop for the love of God.
E♭   **C   F**   **C**
I fought the war, I fought the war
          E♭   **G5**   **B♭**
But the war won't stop for the love of God.
E♭   **C   F**   **C**   **E♭**   **(G5)**
I fought the war, I fought the war but the war won!

Kingdom Of Doom

Words & Music by
Damon Albarn & Paul Simonon

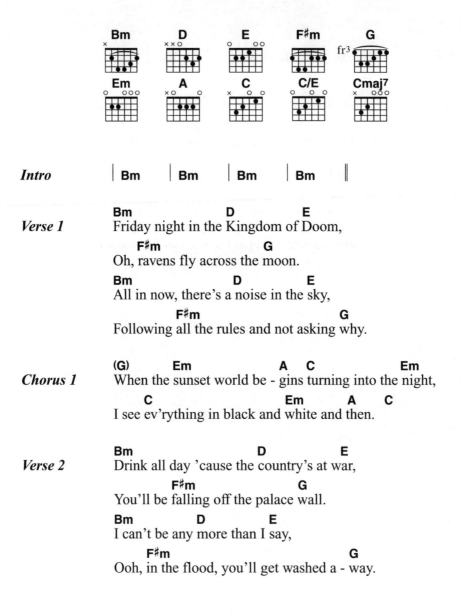

Intro | Bm | Bm | Bm | Bm ‖

Verse 1

Bm   D   E
Friday night in the Kingdom of Doom,
     F#m   G
Oh, ravens fly across the moon.
Bm   D   E
All in now, there's a noise in the sky,
     F#m   G
Following all the rules and not asking why.

Chorus 1

(G)   Em   A C   Em
When the sunset world be - gins turning into the night,
    C   Em   A C
I see ev'rything in black and white and then.

Verse 2

Bm   D   E
Drink all day 'cause the country's at war,
     F#m   G
You'll be falling off the palace wall.
Bm   D   E
I can't be any more than I say,
     F#m   G
Ooh, in the flood, you'll get washed a - way.

Chorus 2

(G)   **Em**   **A**   **C**   **Em**
When the sunset world be - gins turning into the night,

     C   **E**   **A**
I see ev'rything in black and white be - come...

  C   **Em**
A love song for the col - laboration,

C   **Em**   **A**
You and me will never be un - done.

         C
We'll let it blow away,

Outro

‖: **Em** | **C** | **Em** | **C** :‖   *Play 3 times*
  (yeah.)
| **Em** | **C** | **C/E** | **Cmaj⁷** ‖

Mathematics

Words & Music by
Simon Aldred

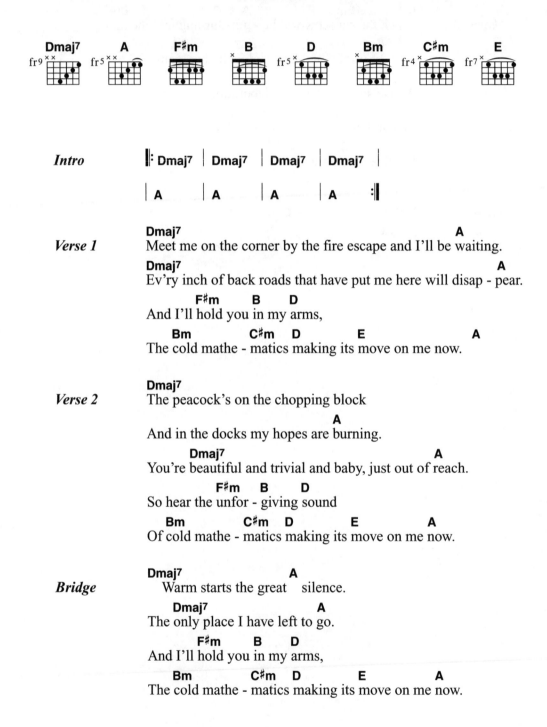

Intro

‖: Dmaj⁷ | Dmaj⁷ | Dmaj⁷ | Dmaj⁷ |

| A | A | A | A :‖

Verse 1

Dmaj⁷   A
Meet me on the corner by the fire escape and I'll be waiting.

Dmaj⁷   A
Ev'ry inch of back roads that have put me here will disap - pear.

        F#m   B   D
And I'll hold you in my arms,

        Bm   C#m   D   E   A
The cold mathe - matics making its move on me now.

Verse 2

Dmaj⁷
The peacock's on the chopping block

                                                    A
And in the docks my hopes are burning.

        Dmaj⁷   A
You're beautiful and trivial and baby, just out of reach.

        F#m   B   D
So hear the unfor - giving sound

        Bm   C#m   D   E   A
Of cold mathe - matics making its move on me now.

Bridge

Dmaj⁷   A
   Warm starts the great   silence.

        Dmaj⁷   A
The only place I have left to go.

        F#m   B   D
And I'll hold you in my arms,

        Bm   C#m   D   E   A
The cold mathe - matics making its move on me now.

Verse 3

Dmaj⁷   **A**
It's funny how I always seem to alienate the people I   like.

Dmaj⁷   **A**
Trying to impress, one day I will learn to shine.

          F♯m   B   D
To the unfor - giving sound

     Bm   C♯m   D   E   A
Of cold mathe - matics making its move on me now.

          F♯m   B   D
And I'll hold you in my arms,

     Bm   C♯m   D   E   A   Dmaj⁷
The cold mathe - matics making its move on me now.

Outro

(Dmaj⁷)   A   Dmaj⁷
Cold mathe - matics making its move.

                A   Dmaj⁷
Cold mathe - matics making its move.

                A   Dmaj⁷   A
Cold mathe - matics making its move.

On Call

Words & Music by
Caleb Followill, Nathan Followill, Jared Followill & Matthew Followill

Em   C   G   Bm   D

Intro | Em | C | G   ‖

(G)   **Em**   **C**   **G**
She said call me now baby, and I'd come a-running.

            Em   **C**   **G**
She said call me now baby, and I'd come a-running.

            Em   **C**
If you'd call me now, baby then I'd come a-running.

| G | Bm | G | Bm |

| G | Bm | G | Bm   ‖

Verse 1   **G**   **Bm**   **G**   **Bm**   **G**
     I'm on call   to be there,   one and all,   to be there.

                   Bm   **G**   **N.C.**
And when I fall   to pieces,   Lord you know,

                   G
I'll be there waiting.

Link 1   **Bm**   **G**   **Bm**
     To be there.

To be there.

Verse 2   **G**   **Bm**   **G**   **Bm**   **G**
     I'm on call   to be there,   one and all,   to be there.

                   Bm   **G**   **N.C.(Bm)**
And when I fall   to pieces,   Lord you know,

I'll be there waiting.

                  G   Bm   G   Bm   G
Verse 3   I'm gon' brawl,   so be there,   one for all,   I'll be there.
                                       Bm   G   N.C.(Bm)
              And when they fall   to pieces,   Lord you know,
                                              G
              I'll be there laughing.

                  (G)   C
Bridge   I'd come a running.
                                         D
              I'd come a running.
                                         Em
              I'd come a running.

Solo | G | G | C | C | D | D   ‖

Link | G | Bm | G | Bm   ‖

Outro | G   ‖
              Bm   G   Bm
                 To be there.
                              G
              To be there.
                        Bm   G
              I'm on call   to be there.
                        Bm   G
              I'm on call   to be there.
                        Bm   G
              I'm on call   to be there.
                        Bm   N.C.
              I'm on call   to be there.

Phantom Limb

Words & Music by
James Mercer

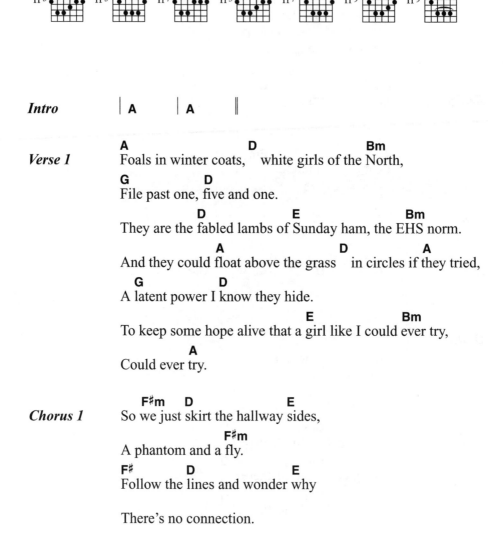

Intro | A | A ‖

Verse 1

    A   D   Bm
Foals in winter coats,   white girls of the North,
  G   D
File past one, five and one.
               D   E   Bm
They are the fabled lambs of Sunday ham, the EHS norm.
                A   D   A
And they could float above the grass   in circles if they tried,
  G   D
A latent power I know they hide.
                   E   Bm
To keep some hope alive that a girl like I could ever try,
         A
Could ever try.

Chorus 1

       F#m   D   E
So we just skirt the hallway sides,
           F#m
A phantom and a fly.
F#   D   E
Follow the lines and wonder why

There's no connection.

Verse 2

   A   D   Bm
A week of rolling eyes   and cheap shots from the trite,

        G   D
And we're off to Nemarca's porch again.

                           E   Bm
Another afternoon with the goat-head tunes and pilfered booze.

        A   D
We wander through her mama's house,

            A   G   D
The milk from the window lights, family portrait circa '95.

                         E   Bm
This is that foreign land of the sprayed-on tans and it all feels fine,

      A
Be it silk or slime.

Chorus 2

   F♯m   D   E
So, when they tap our Monday heads,

                F♯m
Two zombies walk in   our stead.

 F♯   D   E
This town seems hardly worth our time,

   F♯m   D   E
And we'll no long - er memorize or rhyme,

        F♯m
Too far along in our climb.

      F♯   D   E
Stepping over what now towers to the sky,

With no connection.

Bridge

   A   D   E
‖: Ooh, wah ooh, wah ooh.

 A   D   E
Ooh, wah ooh, wah ooh. :‖

Chorus 3

 F♯m   D   E
So, when they tap our Monday heads,

                F♯m
Two zombies walk in   our stead.

F♯   D   E
This town seems hardly worth our time,

   F♯m   D   E
And we'll no long - er memorize or rhyme,

        F♯m
Too far along in our climb.

      F♯   D   E
Stepping over what now towers to the sky,

With no connection.

POD

Words & Music by
Jack Black & Kyle Gass

Am   F   G   E   Dm   C

Chorus 1

N.C.   Am
'Cause it's the pick of destiny child,

 F   G
You know we will be rockin' cause it's fucking insane.

     N.C. Am
It's just the pick of destiny child,

   F   G
More precious than a diamond on a platinum chain.

Verse 1

Am   G F
In Venice Beach, there was a man named Kage,

          G   Am
When he was buskin' he was all the rage.

            G F
He met Jables and he taught him well,

            G   Am
All the techniques that were de - veloped in hell.

           G F
Cock pushups and the power slide,

          G   Am
Gig simulation now there's nowhere to hide.

             G F
They formed a band they named Tenacious D,

          G
And then they got the pick of destiny.

Chorus 2

(G)   N.C. Am
'Cause it's the pick of destiny child,

 F   G
You know we will be rockin' cause it's fucking insane.

     N.C. Am
It's just the pick of destiny child,

   F   G
Our tasty grooves are better than a chicken chow mein.

Bridge 1

         F   G
'Cause he who is sleazy is easy to pleasy.

         F   G
And she who is juicy must be loosy-goosey.

         F   G
And he who is groovy will be in my movie,

         Am   G F G E
So come on!

Interlude

         Dm
The wizard and the demon had a battle royale,

         Am
The demon almost killed him with an evil kapow!

      C   G
But then he broke his tooth and thus the demon said: "Ow."

Chorus 3

(G)   N.C. Am
'Cause it's the pick   of destiny child,

      F   G
You know we will be rockin' cause it's fucking insane.

(G)   N.C. Am
'Cause it's the pick   of destiny child,

      F   G
You know our movie's better than Citizen Kane.

Bridge 2

         F   G
'Cause he who's a geezer must live in my freezer.

         F   G
And she who is starkey is full of malarkey.

         F   G
And he who is groovy must be in my movie,

         Am
So come on!

Solo

| Am | Am G | F | G |
(on!)
| Am | Am G | F | G ||

Bridge 3

(G)   F   G
Oh! 'Cause if you're a diva, then go to Geneva.

        F   G
And if you're a crony, then suck on my bony.

        F   G
And if you are groovy, then get in my movie.

              F   G   Am
It's called the Pick of Desti - ny.

        F   G   Am
The Pick of Desti - ny.

Our Velocity

Words & Music by
Paul Smith, Thomas English, Duncan Lloyd, Archis Tiku & Lukas Wooller

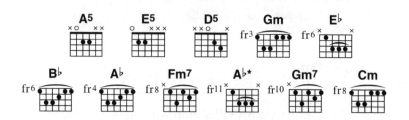

Intro

| N.C. | N.C. A5 | E5 | D5 E5 | A5 E5 | D5 |

| E5 A5 | E5 | D5 E5 | A5 E5 | D5 E5 | A5 |

Verse 1

(A5)   E5 D5   E5 A5   E5   D5 E5
I'm not a man, I'm a ma - chine, chisel me down until I am clean.

A5 E5 D5 E5 A5   E5   D5 E5 A5
I buy books, I never read, and then I'll tell you some more about me.

Link 1

| E5 D5 | E5 A5 | E5 D5 | E5 A5 |

Verse 2

(A5)   E5   D5   E5 A5   E5   D5 E5
Beneath the concrete there's a sound, a muffled cry below the ground.

A5   E5   D5 E5 A5 E5   D5 E5 A5
There is a poison in the air, a mix of chemicals and fear.

E5   D5 E5   A5 E5   D5 E5   A5
Manners are just hunches,   I'm not sure what they mean.

      E5   D5   E5 A5   E5   D5 E5   A5
You're asking for commit - ment when I'm somewhere in be - tween.

Chorus 1

Gm   E♭
Never, never try to gauge temperature,

Gm   E♭ B♭
When you tend to travel at such speed,

      A♭ Gm   E♭ Gm
It's our ve - loci - ty.

                    E♭   B♭
Is it cold where you are this time of the year,

     A♭ N.C. A5
You didn't leave a scar.

Link 2 | E5   D5 | E5   A5 | E5   D5 | E5   A5 |

| E5   D5 | E5   A5 | E5   D5 | E5   A5 ‖

Verse 3

(A5)   E5   D5 E5
A stream of numbers hit a screen

A5   E5   D5   E5
And you're ex - pected to know what they mean.

A5   E5   D5   E5
Throughout the conflict I was se - rene,

A5   E5   D5 E5   A5
I can't out - run the sadness I've seen.

A5   E5   D5   E5 A5   D5   E5   A5
Are you willing to re - sist, the people you've never met.

      E5   D5   E5   A5   E5   D5 E5
The devil's wheel re - volves, but it needs to be re - set.

Chorus 2

Gm   E♭
Never, never try to gauge temperature,

Gm   E♭   B♭
When you tend to travel at such speed,

              A♭   Gm
It's our ve - loci - ty.

          E♭   Gm   B♭   E♭   B♭
Please tell me   is it cold where you are this time of the year,

          A♭   E♭   Fm7 A♭* Gm7
You didn't leave a scar.

Bridge 1

E♭   Fm7   A♭*
I've got no one to call,

                  Gm7   E♭
In the middle of the night any - more,

          Fm7   Cm   B♭ E♭
I'm just a - lone with these thoughts.

                  Fm7   A♭*
I've got no one to call,

                  Gm7   E♭
In the middle of the night any - more,

          Fm7   Cm   B♭
I'm just a - lone with my thoughts.

53

Link 3   ‖: Gm | Gm B♭ E♭ | Gm | Gm E♭ B♭ :‖

Interlude

Gm   B♭   E♭
  I watched a film to change my feel - ings,

Gm   E♭   B♭
  Strong enough to bear a bur - den.

Gm
  If everyone became this sensitive,

I wouldn't have to be so sensitive.

If ev'ryone became so sensitive,

Perhaps I wouldn't be so sensitive.

Bridge 2

E♭   Fm7
Love is a lie, which means I've been lied to,

A♭*   Gm7   E♭
Love is a lie, which means I've been lying too.

    Fm7   Cm
Love is a lie, which means I've been lied to,

   B♭
Love is a lie.

Bridge 3

E♭   Fm7   A♭*
  I've got no one to call,

         Gm7   E♭
In the middle of the night any - more,

     Fm7   Cm   B♭ E♭
I'm just a - lone with these thoughts.

         Fm7   A♭*
I've got no one to call,

         Gm7   E♭
In the middle of the night any - more,

     Fm7   Cm   B♭ E♭
I'm just a - lone with my thoughts.

Chorus 3

Gm   E♭
Never, never try to guage temperature,

         E♭   B♭
When you tend to travel at such speed,

     A♭   N.C.
It's our ve - loci - ty.

Read My Mind

Words & Music by
Brandon Flowers, Dave Keuning, Mark Stoermer & Ronnie Vannucci

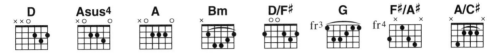

Tune guitar down a semitone

Intro ‖: D | D | Asus⁴ | A :‖

Verse 1

D   Asus⁴
On the corner of main street,

               A   D
Just tryin' to keep it in line.

                                    Asus⁴
You say you wanna move on and

               A
You say I'm falling be - hind.

               D   Bm D/F♯ Asus⁴ A
Can you read my mind?

               D   Bm D/F♯ Asus⁴ A
Can you read my mind?

Verse 2

D   Bm   D/F♯   Asus⁴
I never really gave up   on

               A   D
Breakin' out of this two-star town.

               Bm   D/F♯   Asus⁴
I got the green light, I got a little fight,

                    A
I'm gonna turn this thing a - round.

               D   Bm D/F♯ Asus⁴ A
Can you read my mind?

               D   Bm D/F♯ Asus⁴ A
Can you read my mind?

Pre-chorus 1
```
(A)            G                 D
The good old days, the honest man,
                     A
The restless heart, the Promised Land.
          G              D
A subtle kiss that no one sees,
                A
A broken wrist and a big trapeze.
```

Chorus 1
```
A              G              D
Oh well I don't mind, you don't mind,
                A      F♯/A♯     Bm
'Cause I don't shine if you don't shine,
    D/F♯     G                    A
Be - fore you go can you read my mind?
```

Verse 3
```
D                         Bm   D/F♯    Asus⁴
    It's funny how you just break down,
                    A
Waitin' on some sign.
    D                     Bm    D/F♯    Asus⁴
I pull up to the front of your drive - way
                        A
With magic soakin' my spine.
                    D        Bm  D/F♯  Asus⁴  A
Can you read my mind?
                    D        Bm  D/F♯  Asus⁴  A
Can you read my mind?
```

Pre chorus 2
```
(A)            G                 D
The teenage queen, the loaded gun,
                 A
The drop dead dream, the Chosen One.
         G                    D
A southern drawl and a world un - seen,
           A
A city wall and a trampoline.
```

Chorus 2
```
A              G              D
Oh well I don't mind, you don't mind,
                  A      F♯/A♯     Bm
'Cause I don't shine if you don't shine.
         D/F♯     G
Be - fore you go,
                    A                      Bm
Tell me what you find when you read my mind.
```

Solo | Bm | A | G | D A/C♯ | Bm |

| A | G | A | A | A ||

Pre-chorus 3
   A   G   D
Slippin' in my faith into the fall,
                  A
You never re - turned that call.
                  G   D
Woman, open the door, don't let it sting,
                A
I wanna breathe that fire again.

Bridge
She said:
       Bm   A
"I don't mind, you don't mind,
          G   D
'Cause I don't shine if you don't shine."
       A/C♯   Bm
Put your back on me.
          A
Put your back on me.
          G
Put your back on me.

Outro | D | Bm D/F♯ | Asus4 | A ||
D
   The stars are blazing
       Bm   D/F♯   Asus4   A
Like rebel diamonds cut out of the sun
                D
When you read my mind.

‖: D | Bm D/F♯ | Asus4 | A   :‖
  (mind)
| D ||

Ruby

Words & Music by
Charlie Wilson, Nicholas Hodgson, Andrew White, James Rix & Nicholas Baines

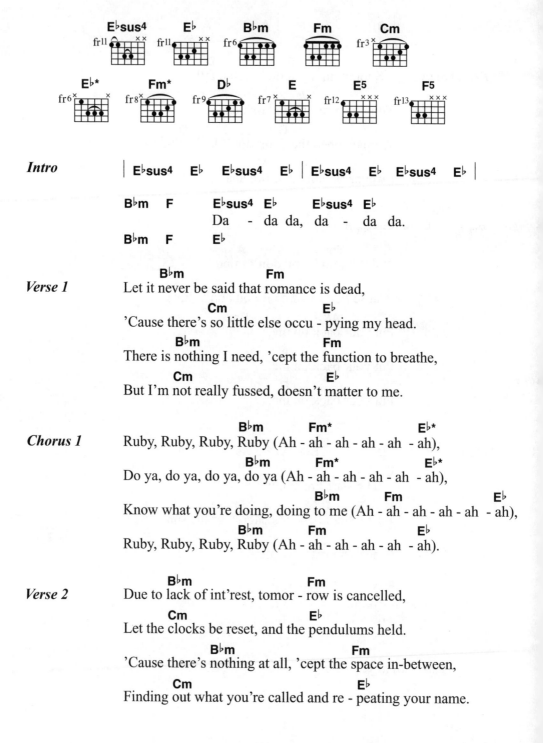

Intro

| E♭sus4 E♭ E♭sus4 E♭ | E♭sus4 E♭ E♭sus4 E♭ |

B♭m　　F　　E♭sus4 E♭　　E♭sus4 E♭

Da - da da, da - da da.

B♭m　　F　　E♭

Verse 1

　　　　　　　　B♭m　　　　　　　　Fm
Let it never be said that romance is dead,

　　　　　　　Cm　　　　　　　　　E♭
'Cause there's so little else occu - pying my head.

　　　　　　　　B♭m　　　　　　　Fm
There is nothing I need, 'cept the function to breathe,

　　　　Cm　　　　　　　　　　　E♭
But I'm not really fussed, doesn't matter to me.

Chorus 1

　　　　　　　　　　　B♭m　　　Fm*　　　　　　　E♭*
Ruby, Ruby, Ruby, Ruby (Ah - ah - ah - ah - ah - ah),

　　　　　　　　　B♭m　　　Fm*　　　　　　E♭*
Do ya, do ya, do ya, do ya (Ah - ah - ah - ah - ah - ah),

　　　　　　　　　　　　B♭m　　　Fm　　　　　　　　E♭
Know what you're doing, doing to me (Ah - ah - ah - ah - ah - ah),

　　　　　　　　　　B♭m　　　Fm　　　　E♭
Ruby, Ruby, Ruby, Ruby (Ah - ah - ah - ah - ah - ah).

Verse 2

　　　　　　B♭m　　　　　　　　　　Fm
Due to lack of int'rest, tomor - row is cancelled,

　　　Cm　　　　　　　　　E♭
Let the clocks be reset, and the pendulums held.

　　　　　　　B♭m　　　　　　　　Fm
'Cause there's nothing at all, 'cept the space in-between,

　　　Cm　　　　　　　　　　　E♭
Finding out what you're called and re - peating your name.

B♭m   Fm*   E♭*
Ruby, Ruby, Ruby, Ruby (Ah - ah - ah - ah - ah - ah),
       B♭m   Fm*   E♭*
Do ya, do ya, do ya, do ya (Ah - ah - ah - ah - ah - ah),
         B♭m   Fm   E♭
Know what you're doing, doing to me (Ah - ah - ah - ah - ah - ah),
     B♭m   Fm   E♭   E
Ruby, Ruby, Ruby, Ruby (Ah - ah - ah - ah - ah - ah).

Fm   D♭
   Could it be, could it be, that you're joking with me,
     B♭m   E♭*   E
And you don't really see you with me.
Fm   D♭
   Could it be, could it be, that you're joking with me,
     B♭m   E♭*   E
And you don't really see you with me.

‖: F | D♭ | B♭m | E♭m   E   :‖ F |

B♭m   Fm*   E♭*
Ruby, Ruby, Ruby, Ruby (Ah - ah - ah - ah - ah - ah),
       B♭m   Fm*   E♭*
Do ya, do ya, do ya, do ya (Ah - ah - ah - ah - ah - ah),
         B♭m   Fm   E♭
Know what you're doing, doing to me (Ah - ah - ah - ah - ah - ah),
     B♭m   Fm   E♭
Ruby, Ruby, Ruby, Ruby (Ah - ah - ah - ah - ah - ah).
       B♭m
And do ya, do ya, do ya, do ya,
   Fm   E♭sus4 E♭   E♭sus4 E♭
(Ah - ah - ah - ah - ah - ah),
      (Da - da da, da - da da.)
       B♭m
Know what you're doing, doing to me,
   Fm   E♭sus4 E♭   E   F5
(Ah - ah - ah - ah - ah - ah).
      (Da - da da.)

Same Jeans

Words & Music by
Kyle Falconer & Keiren Webster

C **Fadd9** **G** **C*** **G5** **F** **C/G**

Intro | C Fadd9 | G C | C Fadd9 | G C

Verse 1
              C   Fadd9   G   C
I've had the same jeans on   for four days now,
            C   Fadd9   G   C
I'm gonna go to a disco in the middle of the town.
           C   Fadd9 G   C
Ev'rybo - dy's dressing up, I'm dressing down.

| C Fadd9 | G C

Verse 2
C   Fadd9   G   C
Life's one big circle and it does end,
            C   Fadd9   G   C
When it ends   will you still be my friend?
C   Fadd9   G   C
Am I making a fool of my - self? Oh, tell me,
C   Fadd9   G5   C*
I'm not making a fool of my - self.

Chorus
        C*   F   C* F
So, when you look in the mirror,
      C*   F   G
Re - flecting back at you   someone that you don't know.
C*   F   C*   F
  That shit's made your head   spin around,
     C*   F   G5
So get yourself togeth - er and get your feet back on the ground.

Verse 3   As Verse 1

Verse 4

```
        C          Fadd9  G      C
I take my hat(s) off to the   busker man,
              C              Fadd9  G        C
When he drowns   all his sor - rows on singin' a song,
        C         Fadd9   G               C
Not ev - 'rything       has worked out to plan,
            C          Fadd9     G5        C*
But believe    me he's smiling as long as he can.
```

Chorus 2   As Chorus 1

Solo   ‖: C*   F │ C*   F │ C*   F │ G5   :‖

│ G5   │
        (I've had the)

Verse 5   As Verse 1

Verse 6

```
        C          Fadd9    G      C
My mind's not perfect but it's sin - cere,
              C              Fadd9       G   C
You'd be a - mazed at what you can achieve   in a year.
            C   Fadd9            G      C
Now you tried   so hard, but your heart's   on a switch.
        C              Fadd9          G5    C*
And I know you try so hard, But your heart's   on a switch.
```

Chorus 3   ‖: As Chorus 1 :‖

Interlude   │ C*   F │ G   C/G │ C   Fadd9 │ C   Fadd9 │ C   Fadd9 │ C ‖

Outro

```
    C*                    F
‖: Same Jeans on for four   days now,
        C*                       F
Ev'ry - body's dressing up I'm dress - ing down,
C*            F
Am I making a fool   of myself,
        C*            F
Now be - lieve me lady, I   can't tell. :‖
```

│ C*   F │ C*   F │ C*   F │ G   C/G   ‖

Roscoe

Words & Music by
Timothy Smith

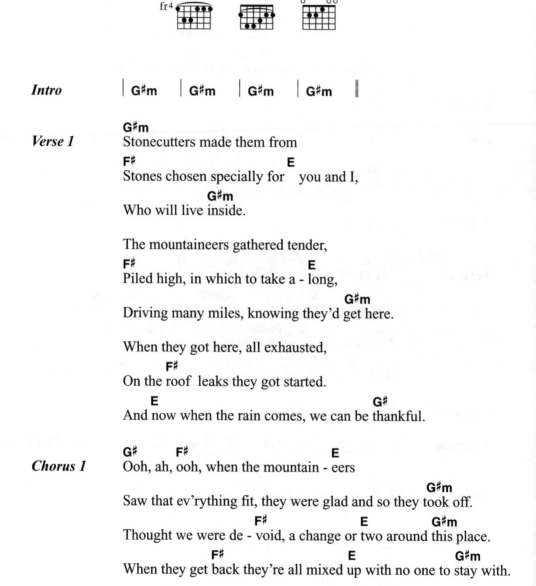

G♯m   F♯   E

Intro | G♯m | G♯m | G♯m | G♯m ||

Verse 1

G♯m
Stonecutters made them from
F♯   E
Stones chosen specially for   you and I,
           G♯m
Who will live inside.

The mountaineers gathered tender,
F♯   E
Piled high, in which to take a - long,
                         G♯m
Driving many miles, knowing they'd get here.

When they got here, all exhausted,
      F♯
On the roof leaks they got started.
     E   G♯
And now when the rain comes, we can be thankful.

Chorus 1

G♯   F♯   E
Ooh, ah, ooh, when the mountain - eers
                                       G♯m
Saw that ev'rything fit, they were glad and so they took off.
                   F♯   E   G♯m
Thought we were de - void, a change or two around this place.
          F♯   E   G♯m
When they get back they're all mixed up with no one to stay with.

Link 1 | G♯m | G♯m | F♯ |

              | F♯ | E | E   ‖
                                              (The village)

                               G♯m
Verse 2   The village used to be all one really needs,
                                       F♯
              Now it's filled with hundreds and hundreds of chemicals,
                                     E
              That mostly sur - round you.
                                                              G♯m
              You wish to flee, but it's not like you, so listen to me, listen to me.

              Oh, oh, and when the morning comes, we will step outside,
                         F♯
              We will not find another man inside.
                                              E
              We like the newness, the new - ness of all
                                                      G♯m
              That has grown in our garden soaking for so   long.

              Whenever I was a child I wondered what if my name had changed
                    F♯
              Into something more productive like Roscoe,
                              E   G♯m
              Been born in eighteen ninety-one, waiting with my Aunt Rosaline.

              G♯m   F♯
Chorus 2   Thought we were de - void,
                             E   G♯m
              A change or two around this place.
                          F♯   E   G♯m
              When they get back they're all mixed up with no one to stay with.

Interlude | G♯m | G♯m | F♯ | F♯ | E | E |

              | G♯m | G♯m | G♯m | G♯m | F♯ | E | E   ‖

63

Verse 3

     E   **G♯m**
Eighteen ninety-one,

                       F♯
They roamed around in the forests.

                  E
They made their house from cedars,

                  G♯m
They made their house from stones.

             F♯
Oh, they're a little like you,

                E
And they're a little like me,

     G♯m
We are falling leaves.

Chorus 3

 G♯m   **F♯**
Thought we were de - void,

            E   **G♯m**
A change or two around this place,

   F♯   **E**   **G♯m**
This place, this place._____

G♯m   **F♯**   **E**
When they get back they're all mixed up

                 G♯m
With no one to stay   with.

            F♯   **E**
When they get back they're all mixed up

               G♯m
With no one to stay with.

Save Myself

Words & Music by
Willy Mason

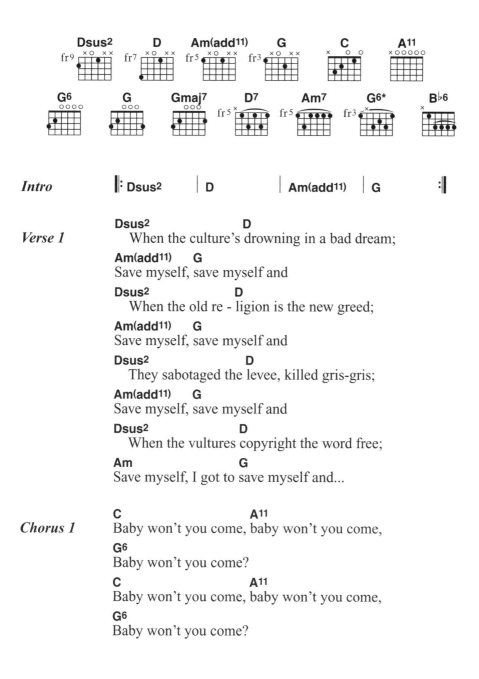

Intro ‖: Dsus2 | D | Am(add11) | G :‖

Verse 1

Dsus2   D
When the culture's drowning in a bad dream;
Am(add11)   G
Save myself, save myself and
Dsus2   D
When the old re - ligion is the new greed;
Am(add11)   G
Save myself, save myself and
Dsus2   D
They sabotaged the levee, killed gris-gris;
Am(add11)   G
Save myself, save myself and
Dsus2   D
When the vultures copyright the word free;
Am   G
Save myself, I got to save myself and...

Chorus 1

C   A11
Baby won't you come, baby won't you come,
G6
Baby won't you come?
C   A11
Baby won't you come, baby won't you come,
G6
Baby won't you come?

Verse 2

Dsus²   D
When the elders all are playing make believe;

Am(add¹¹)   G
Save myself, I got to save myself and

Dsus²   D
When they teach us lessons that they don't believe;

Am(add¹¹)   G
Save myself, I got to save myself and

Dsus²   D
When they build up statues but neglect their seed;

Am(add¹¹)   G
Save myself, I got to save myself and

Dsus²   D
When my love and my hammer's all I really need;

Am(add¹¹)   G
Save myself, I got to save myself and...

Chorus 2

C   A¹¹
Baby won't you come, baby won't you come,

G⁶   G
Baby won't you come?

C   A¹¹
Baby won't you come, baby won't you come,

Gmaj⁷
Baby won't you come?

Bridge

G⁶   D⁷
Baby won't you come slow and steady?

Am⁷   G⁶*   B♭6
Slow and steady, slow and steady, slow and steady.

D⁷   Am⁷   G⁶*   B♭6
Slow and steady, slow and steady, slow and steady, slow and steady.

Verse 3

Dsus²   D
When I live in a country without history;

Am(add¹¹)   G
Save myself, I got to save myself and

Dsus²   D
One that buried its roots with its identity;

Am(add¹¹)   G
Save myself, I got to save myself and

Dsus²   D
We still are searching for liberty;

cont.

Am(add11)   **G**
Save myself, I got to save myself and

Dsus2   **D**
  We still are hiding from reality;

Am   **G**
Save myself, I got to save myself and...

Outro

C   **A11**
Baby won't you come, baby won't you come,

G6
Baby won't you come?

C   **A11**
Baby won't you come, baby won't you come,

G6
Baby won't you come,

G
Baby won't you come?

C   **A11**
Baby won't you come, baby won't you come,

G6
Baby won't you come?

C   **A11**
Baby won't you come, baby won't you come,

G6
Baby won't you come,

G
Baby won't you come?

C   **A11**
Baby won't you come, baby won't you come,

G6
Baby won't you come,

G
Baby won't you come?

C   **A11**
Baby won't you come, baby won't you come,

G6
Baby won't you come,

G   **C**
Baby won't you come?

Standing In The Way Of Control

Words & Music by
Beth Ditto, Hannah Blilie and Brace Paine

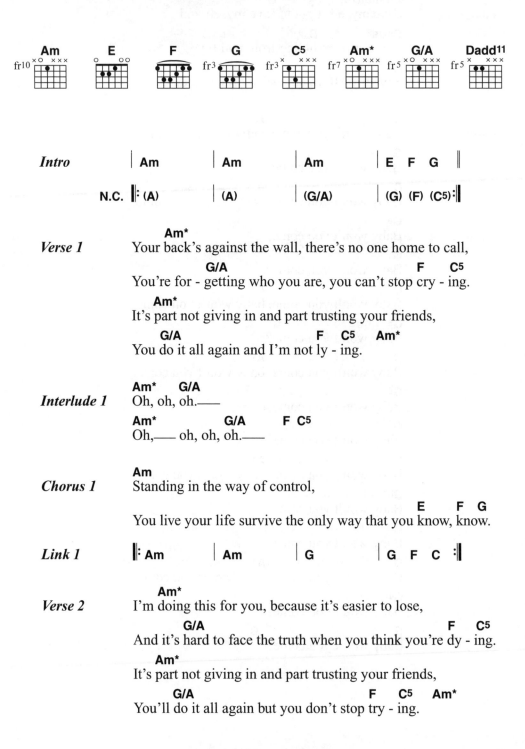

Intro　　　　| Am　　| Am　　| Am　　| E　F　G ‖

N.C. ‖: (A)　　| (A)　　| (G/A)　　| (G) (F) (C5) :‖

Verse 1
　　　　　　　Am*
Your back's against the wall, there's no one home to call,
　　　　　　　G/A　　　　　　　　　　　　　**F　　C5**
You're for - getting who you are, you can't stop cry - ing.
　　　　　　Am*
It's part not giving in and part trusting your friends,
　　　　G/A　　　　　　　　**F　C5　Am***
You do it all again and I'm not ly - ing.

Interlude 1
　　　　　Am*　　**G/A**
Oh, oh, oh.——
　　　　　Am*　　　　　　**G/A**　　**F　C5**
Oh,—— oh, oh, oh.——

Chorus 1
　　　　Am
Standing in the way of control,
　　　　　　　　　　　　　　　　　　　　　E　　　**F　G**
You live your life survive the only way that you know, know.

Link 1　　‖: Am　　| Am　　| G　　| G　F　C :‖

Verse 2
　　　　　　　Am*
I'm doing this for you, because it's easier to lose,
　　　　G/A　　　　　　　　　　　　　　　　**F　　C5**
And it's hard to face the truth when you think you're dy - ing.
　　　　　　Am*
It's part not giving in and part trusting your friends,
　　　　G/A　　　　　　　　　**F　C5　Am***
You'll do it all again but you don't stop try - ing.

	G/A **F C5**

Interlude 2
```
             G/A          F C5
         Oh, oh, oh.——

         Am*             GA         F C5
         Oh,—— oh, oh, oh.——
```

Chorus 2
```
         Am
         Standing in the way of control,

                                              E      F   G
         You live your life survive the only way that you know, know.
```

Link 2
```
         ‖: Am        | Am        | G/A       | C5 Dadd11 :‖
```

Interlude 2
```
         Am            G/A        C5 Dadd11
         Oh,—— oh, oh, oh.——

         Am            G/A        C5 Dadd11
         Oh,—— oh, oh, oh.——
```

Bridge 1
```
         Am
         Standing in the way of control,

             G/A           C5
         We live our lives,

             Dadd11  Am
         Be - cause of standing in the way of control.

             G/A           C5
         We will live our lives,

             Dadd11  Am
         Be - cause of standing in the way of control.

             G/A           C5
         We'll live our lives,

             Dadd11  Am
         Be - cause of standing in the way of control.

             G/A              C5         Dadd11   Am
         We will live our lives, lives, lives, ooh.

             E   F   G
         Oh, hey, yeah.
```

Link 3
```
         ‖: Am        | Am        | G/A       | G   F   C5 :‖
```

Verse 3
Am*
Your back's against the wall, there's no one home to call,
        G/A   **F**   **C5**
You're for - getting who you are, you can't stop cry - ing.
      Am*
It's part not giving in, and part trusting your friends,
       G/A   **F**   **C5**   **Am***
You'll do it all again, you don't stop try - ing.

Interlude 3
         G/A   **F C5**
Oh, oh, oh.——
Am*   **G/A**   **F C5**
Oh,—— oh, oh, oh.——

Chorus 3
Am
Standing in the way of control,
                                    E   **F** **G**   **Am**
You live your life survive the only way that you know, know.

Starz In Their Eyes

Words & Music by
Jack Allsopp

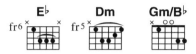

Intro 𝄆 Eb | Dm Gm/Bb | Eb | Dm Gm/Bb 𝄇

Verse 1
     Eb   **Dm**
They'll be making sure you stay a - mused,
    Gm/Bb   **Eb**
They'll fill you up with drugs and booze,
                         Dm   **Gm/Bb** **Eb**
Maybe you'll make the evening news.
                              Dm
And when you're tripping over your dreams,
    Gm/Bb   **Eb**
They'll keep you down by any means,
                     Dm   **Gm/Bb**
By the end of the night you'll be stifling your screams.

Pre-chorus 1
  Eb   **Dm**
And since you became a V. I. Person,
  Gm/Bb   **Eb**
It's like your problems have all worsened,
             Dm   **Gm/Bb**   **Eb**
Your paranoia casts as - persions on the truths you know.
                    Dm   **Gm/Bb**
And they'll just put you in the spotlight,
              Eb   **Dm** **Gm/Bb**
And hope that you'll do alright, or maybe not.

Chorus 1

E♭   Dm   Gm/B♭
Now why do you wanna go and put starz in their eyes?

E♭   Dm   Gm/B♭
Why do you wanna go and put starz in their eyes?

   E♭   Dm   Gm/B♭
So why do you wanna go and put starz in their eyes?

    E♭   Dm
Now why do you wanna go and put starz in their eyes?

Gm/B♭
Starz in their eyes?

Verse 2

E♭   Dm
  Remember they said you'd show them all,

       Gm/B♭   E♭
Emphasise the rise but not the fall,

                 Dm   Gm/B♭   E♭
And now you're playing a shopping mall.

                 Dm
Your mum and dad they can't believe

       Gm/B♭   E♭
What you ap - pear to have a - chieved,

               Dm   Gm/B♭
While the rest of these users are just laughing in their sleeves.

Pre-chorus 2

E♭   Dm
  And since you became a V. I. Person,

      Gm/B♭   E♭
It's like your problems have all worsened.

           Dm   Gm/B♭   E♭
Your paranoia casts as - persions on the truths you know.

             Dm
And now the tabloids use your face

    Gm/B♭   E♭
To docu - ment your fall from grace,

                 Dm   Gm/B♭   E♭
And then they'll tell you that that's just the way it goes,

       Dm   E♭
That's just the way it goes.

Bridge 1

    E♭   Dm   Gm/B♭
Now why do you wanna go and put starz in their eyes?

     E♭   Dm   Gm/B♭
It's the same old story, well they just didn't realise.

      E♭
And it's a long way to come from

  Dm   Gm/B♭   E♭
The Dog and Duck   karaoke machine

          Dm   Gm/B♭
And Saturday night's drunken dreams.

Bridge 2	E♭ Dm Gm/B♭

Bridge 2

E♭   Dm   Gm/B♭
Now why do you wanna go and put starz in their eyes?

E♭   Dm   Gm/B♭
It's the same old story, well they just didn't realise.

E♭
And it's a long way to come from your

Dm   Gm/B♭   E♭
Private bed - room dance rou - tines

Dm   Gm/B♭
And Saturday night's drunken dreams.

Chorus 2   As Chorus 1

Bridge 3   As Bridge 1

spoken: *When I grow up I'm gonna be famous.*

Rap

(Gm/B♭)
Behind the steel barrier and sequins and glitter ,
Five inch heels still knee deep in the litter,
Each of them a bitter bullshitter.
Wrapped up in the cloak of fake glamour,
Getting lost in the camera.
And diamond crusts on their one-off plimsolls,
So little time for these one-off arseholes.
Rigor mortis Ken and Barbie dolls,
A pair of big shades and a push up bra,
It's such a short gap between the gutter and stars.
But you've come a long way from the place that you started,
So why'd you wanna go and get so downhearted?
Welcome to the kingdom of the blagger,
Uncutting your nose clean, coating you bladder.
A whole lot happier, a whole lot sadder,
Used to be satisfied but now you feel like Mick Jagger.

Interlude   ‖: E♭ | Dm   Gm/B♭ | E♭ | Dm   Gm/B♭ :‖ *Play 4 times*

Bridge 4   As Bridge 1

Bridge 5   As Bridge 2

Stay The Night

Words & Music by
Robert Smith, Simon Pettigrew, Edward Harris & Mark Treasure

Intro | F#m | F#m | F#m | F#m ‖

Verse 1

F#m
It's four o'clock in the morning,

    D5   D(♭5)   Bm7
I can't take another second of this excuse for text.

   C#m   F#m
Take a chance and stay the night.

              D5
Oh, why don't we take a taxi back to mine,

        D(♭5)   Bm7
I'm sure that we'll find a way to pass the time.

   C#m7   F#m
Take a chance and stay the night.

Chorus 1

   B   D#m   B
  If it's a question of tim - ing, I'll wait.

         D#m   B
If there's a reason or rhyme, I'll wait.

      D#m   G#m
I gave you the night 'cause I know what I found.

       F#sus4 F#   F#m
I think of you, my heartbeat's a little louder.

(F#m)   D7 D6 D7
A little loud - er.

F#m   **D5**
I can't decide if you're giving me a sign,
                                        D(♭5)   **Bm7**
Well maybe you're just like this all the time.
              C#m7   **F#m**
Take a chance and stay the night.

                                                                  D5
Oh, please don't tell me you're worried, you might find
                                        D(♭5)   **Bm7**
When morning comes, the re - gret you caused that night.
              C#m7   **F#m**
Take a chance and stay the night.

Chorus 2
B   **D#m**   **B**
   If it's a question of tim - ing, I'll wait.
                            D#m   **B**
If there's a reason or rhyme, I'll wait.
                  D#m   **G#m**
I gave you the night 'cause I know what I found.
                    F#sus4   **F#**
I think of you, my heartbeat's a little louder.

Chorus 3
B   **D#m**   **B**
   If it's a question of tim - ing, I'll wait.
                            D#m   **B**
If there's a reason or rhyme, I'll wait.
                  D#m   **G#m**
I gave you the night 'cause I know what I found.
                    F#sus4   **F#**   **E**
I think of you, my heartbeat's a little louder.

Bridge 1
        B   **F#/A#**   **G#m**
My heartbeat's a little louder.
                    F#m/A#   **F#**   **E**
I tell you my heartbeat's a little loud - er.
        B **F#/A#**   **B**
And oh, stay the night.

Outro
(B)   **D#m**   **B**
Stay the night, stay the night.
                        D#m   **B**
Come on stay the night, oh.——
        D#m   **B**
Stay the night.
        D#m   **B**
Stay the night, oh.——

Superstar Tradesman

Words & Music by
Kyle Falconer & Keiren Webster

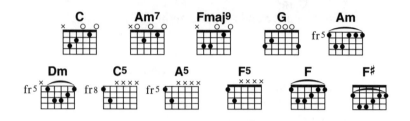

Intro

‖: C   Am7 | C   Am7 :‖

‖: C   Am7 | Fmaj9   C :‖

Verse 1

C   Am7   Fmaj9   C
Superstar tradesman,   stand at the bar.

          Am7   Fmaj9   C
And get a trade   son,   you will go far.

        Fmaj9   G   Fmaj9   G
You'll have a   house in the Fer - ry,   and a new guitar,

Chorus 1

               C   Am7   Fmaj9   C
That's never been played before,   and it never will,

          C   Am7   Fmaj9   C
Never been played before,   and it never will.

Bridge 1

Am   G
The weather is sunny,

Am   G
You're locked inside,

Am   G
The weather is sunny oh yes,

Am   G
I've tried and I've   tried,

Chorus 2

          C   Am7   Fmaj9   C
To keep me sane,   to keep me sane,

          C   Am7   Fmaj9   C
To keep me sane,   to keep me sane.

Bridge 2

Am   G
I don't want money,

     Am   G
I want a thing called happiness,

Am   G
I don't want cash you know,

    Am   G
I'd quite like memories,

Chorus 3

           C   Am⁷ Fmaj⁹   C
To keep us on   track,   let's never look   back,

          Am⁷ Fmaj⁹   C   Am⁷
Keep us on track,   let's never look back.

Middle 8

Dm   Am
What would you do,

Dm   Am
If I asked you?

Dm   Am
What would you do,

Dm   Am
If I asked you?

Chorus 4

           C Am⁷ Fmaj⁹   C
To sail away,   to see some sights?

        C   Am⁷ Fmaj⁹   C
Sail away   with me,   to see some sights?

Interlude   ‖: C   Am⁷ | Fmaj⁹ C :‖

Verse 2

C⁵   A⁵   F⁵   C⁵
  Superstar trades - man,   stand at the bar.

             A⁵   F⁵   C⁵
And get a trade   son, you will go far.

            F   G F♯ F   N.C.
You'll have a   house in the Fer - ry,   and a new guitar,

                C   Am⁷ Fmaj⁹   C
That's never been played before,   and it never will,

             C   Am⁷ Fmaj⁹   C
Never been played before,   and it never will.

Outro   ‖: C   Am⁷ | Fmaj⁹ C :‖

            | C⁵   A⁵ | F⁵ C⁵   ‖

Survivalism

Words & Music by
Trent Reznor

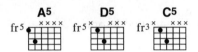

Intro   ‖: A5 | A5 | A5 | A5 :‖

Verse 1
A5
I should have listened to her, so hard to keep control.

We kept on eating but our bloated belly's still not full.

She gave us all she had but we went and took some more.

Can't seem to shut her legs; our mother nature is a whore.

Chorus 1
D5   C5   A5
 I got my propagan - da, I got revision - ism.
D5   C5   A5
 I got my violence in hi-def ultra-real - ism.
D5   C5   A5
 All a part of this great nation.
D5   C5   A5
 I got my fist, I got my prayer, I got survival - ism.

Link 1 | A5 | A5 | A5 | A5 ‖
(-ism)

Verse 2
A5
Hypnotic sound of sirens echoing through the street.

The cocking of the rifles, the marching of the feet.

You see your world on fire, don't try to act surprised.

We did just what you told us

Lost our faith along the way and found ourselves believing your lies.

Chorus 2   As Chorus 1

Link 2   ‖: A5 | A5 | A5 | A5   :‖

Verse 3
A
All bruised and broken, bleeding, she asked to take my hand.

I turned, just keep on walking.

But you'd do the same thing in the circumstance,

I'm sure you'll understand.

Chorus 3
(D5)   (C5)   A5
  I got my propagan - da, I got revision - ism.
D5   C5   A5
  I got my violence in hi-def ultra-real - ism.
D5   C5   A5
  All a part of this great nation.
D5   C5   A5
  I got my fist, I got my prayer, I got survival - ism.

Outro | A5 | A5 | A5 | A5   ‖
(-ism)

‖: A5 | A5 | A5 | A5   :‖ *Play 8 times*
(with ad lib. vocals)

This Ain't A Scene It's An Arms Race

Words & Music by
Peter Wentz, Andrew Hurley, Joseph Trohman & Patrick Stumph

Am   E   F   C   E/G♯   Dm

Intro | Am   ‖

Verse 1

Am
I am an arms dealer,

                 E
Fitting you with weapons in the form of words.

Am
And I don't really care which side wins,

     E
As long as the room keeps singing,

That's just the business I'm in.

Pre-chorus 1

Am
This ain't a scene, it's a Goddamned arms race.

E
This ain't a scene, it's a Goddamned arms race.

Am
This ain't a scene, it's a Goddamned arms race.

E
I'm not a shoulder to cry on, but I digress.

Chorus 1

Am
I'm a leading man,

          F   **C**   **E/G♯**
And the lies I weave are oh so intri - cate, oh so intri - cate.

Am
I'm a leading man,

          F   **C**   **E/G♯**   **Am**
And the lies I weave are oh so intri - cate, oh so intri - cate.

Verse 2

Am
I wrote the gospel of giving up, (you look pretty sinking)

     E
But the real bombshells have already sunk.

(Prima Donnas of the gutter).

   Am
At night we're painting your trash gold while you sleep,

     E
Crashing not like hips or hearts, no, more like p-p-p-parties.

Pre-chorus 2

Am
This ain't a scene, it's a Goddamned arms race.

E
This ain't a scene, it's a Goddamned arms race.

Am
This ain't a scene, it's a Goddamned arms race.

E
Bandwagon's full. Please, catch another.

Chorus 2

Am
I'm a leading man,

       F   C   E/G♯
And the lies I weave are oh so intri - cate, oh so intri - cate.

Am
I'm a leading man,

       F   C   E/G♯
And the lies I weave are oh so intri - cate, oh so intri - cate.

Interlude

| Dm | Am | E | Am | |

| Dm | Am | E | E | ‖

Verse 3

Am
   All the boys who the dance floor didn't love,

                        E
And all the girls whose lips couldn't move fast enough,

Sing until your lungs give out.

Pre-chorus 3

Am
This ain't a scene, it's a Goddamned arms race.

E
This ain't a scene, it's a Goddamned arms race. (Now you.)

Am
This ain't a scene, it's a Goddamned arms race. (Wear out the groove

E
This ain't a scene, it's a Goddamned arms race. (Sing out loud.)

N.C.
This ain't a scene, it's a Goddamned arms race. (Oh, oh.)

This ain't a scene, it's a Goddamned arms race.

Chorus 3

Am
I'm a leading man,

       F   C   E/G♯
And the lies I weave are oh so intri - cate, oh so intri - cate.

Am
I'm a leading man,

       F   C
And the lies I weave are oh so intri - cate,

       E/G♯   E   Am
Oh so intri - cate.

We Used To Vacation

Words & Music by
Nathan Willett, Matthew Maust, Jonathan Russell & Matthew Aveiro

Am   Am/G#   Am/G   Am/F#   F   C   G

Intro ‖: Am | Am/G# | Am/G | Am/F# :‖

Verse 1
Am   Am/G#   Am/G
I kissed the kids at noon   then stumbled out the room.
         Am/F#   Am
I caught a cab, ran up a tab on 7th and flower.
                        Am/G#   Am/G
Beth's recital I had to run,   missed my son's gradua - tion.
                     Am/F#
Punched the Nichols boy for taking his seat,
                    Am
He gets all that anger from me.

Pre-chorus 1
Am   Am/G#
Still, things could be much worse,
           Am/G   Am/F#   Am
Natural disa - sters, on the evening news.
                          Am/G#
Still things could be much worse,
           Am/G   Am/F#   F
We still got our health, my paycheck in the mail.

Chorus 1
F   C   G   F
I promised to my wife and children
                   C   G   F
I'd never touch a - nother drink as long as I live.
                 C   G   F
But even then it sounds so soothing,

This will blow over in time,
                   (Am)
This will all blow over in time.

Link 1   ‖: Am | Am/G♯ | Am/G | Am/F♯ :‖

Verse 2

Am   Am/G♯   Am/G
   I'm just an honest man, provide for me and mine,
                     Am/F♯   Am
I give a check to tax deductible charity organi - zations.
                        Am/G♯   Am/G
Two weeks paid vaca - tion, won't heal the damage done,
             Am/F♯
I need another one.

Pre-chorus 2   As Pre-chorus 1

Chorus 2

F   C   G   F
I promised to my wife and children
                       C   G   F
I'd never touch an - other drink as long as I live.
                 C   G   F
But even then it sounds so soothing,
                   C   G   F
To mix a gin and sink into o - blivion.

Chorus 3

F   C   G   F
I promised to my wife and children,
              C   G   F
That accident left ev'ryone a little shook up.
               C   G   F
But at the meetings I felt so empty.

This will blow over in time,
                          (Am)
This will all blow over in time.

Outro   ‖: Am | Am/G♯ | Am | Am/G♯ :‖

‖: Am | Am/G♯ | Am/G | Am/F♯ :‖   *Repeat ad lib.*

Window In The Skies

Words & Music by
U2

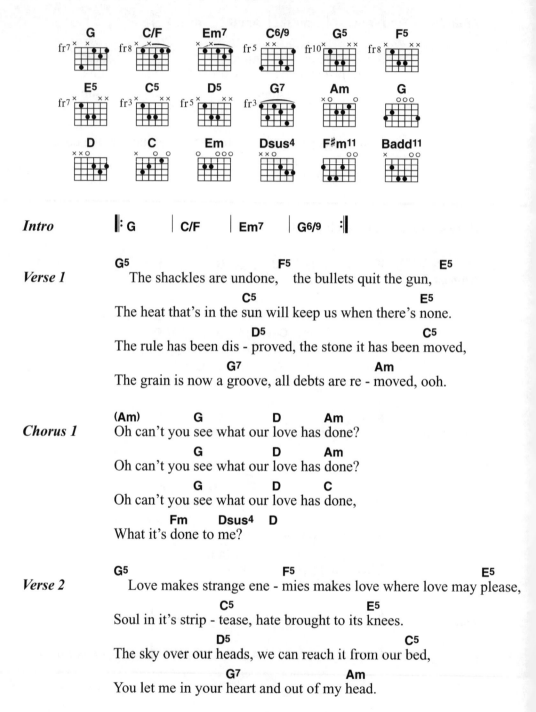

Intro   ‖: G | C/F | Em7 | G6/9 :‖

Verse 1

G5
   The shackles are undone,   the bullets quit the gun, F5 E5

                    C5   E5
The heat that's in the sun will keep us when there's none.

                 D5   C5
The rule has been dis - proved, the stone it has been moved,

              G7   Am
The grain is now a groove, all debts are re - moved, ooh.

Chorus 1

(Am)   G   D   Am
Oh can't you see what our love has done?

              G   D   Am
Oh can't you see what our love has done?

              G   D   C
Oh can't you see what our love has done,

         Fm   Dsus4 D
What it's done to me?

Verse 2

G5   F5   E5
   Love makes strange ene - mies makes love where love may please,

                 C5   E5
Soul in it's strip - tease, hate brought to its knees.

              D5   C5
The sky over our heads, we can reach it from our bed,

                 G7   Am
You let me in your heart and out of my head.

Chorus 2   As Chorus 1

Bridge
F#m11   Badd11
Oh, oh, oh, oh.
F#m11   Badd11
Oh, oh, oh, oh.
C   (G5)
Please don't ever let me out of you.

Interlude | G5 | F5 | E5 | C   ‖
                  here
                C   G5   F5
                I've got no shame,——
                    E5   Am
                Oh no, oh no.

Chorus 3   As Chorus 1

Chorus 4
                          G   D   Am
Oh, I know I hurt you and I made you cry,
                          G   D   Am
Do ev'rything but murder you and I.
G   D   C   Em
But love left a window in the skies,
    Dsus4   D
And to love I rhapso - dize.

Chorus 5
                          G   D   Am
Oh can't you see what love has done to ev'ry broken heart?
                          G   D   Am
Oh can't you see what love has done for ev'ry heart that cries?
G   D   C   Em
Love left a window in the skies,
    Dsus4   D
And to love I rhapso - dize.

Outro
G   C/F   Em7
  Oh,—— oh——
    C6/9   G
Oh,—— oh can't you see?
        C/F   Em7
Oh,—— oh,——
C6/9   G
Oh.

85

Stop Me

Words & Music by
Morrissey & Johnny Marr

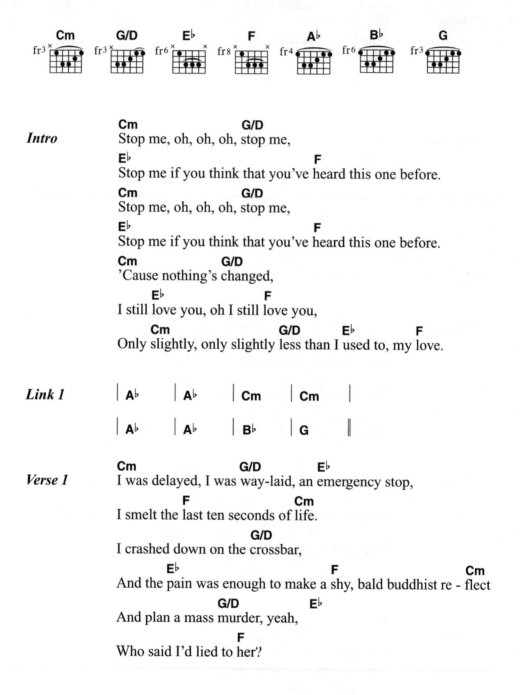

Intro

Cm   G/D
Stop me, oh, oh, oh, stop me,

E♭   F
Stop me if you think that you've heard this one before.

Cm   G/D
Stop me, oh, oh, oh, stop me,

E♭   F
Stop me if you think that you've heard this one before.

Cm   G/D
'Cause nothing's changed,

      E♭   F
I still love you, oh I still love you,

      Cm   G/D   E♭   F
Only slightly, only slightly less than I used to, my love.

Link 1

| A♭ | A♭ | Cm | Cm | |

| A♭ | A♭ | B♭ | G | ‖

Verse 1

Cm   G/D   E♭
I was delayed, I was way-laid, an emergency stop,

                F   Cm
I smelt the last ten seconds of life.

                     G/D
I crashed down on the crossbar,

        E♭   F   Cm
And the pain was enough to make a shy, bald buddhist re - flect

                 G/D   E♭
And plan a mass murder, yeah,

                    F
Who said I'd lied to her?

Chorus 1

Cm   G/D
Who said I'd lied? 'Cause I never, I never.
E♭   F
Who said I'd lied? Because I never.

Link 2   As Link 1

Verse 2

Cm   G/D
I was detained, I was restrained,
                            E♭
And broke my knee and broke my spleen
                            F   Cm
And then he really laid into me, yeah.
                            G/D   E♭
Friday night in out-patients
                                      F
Who said I'd lied to her?

Chorus 2

Cm   G/D   E♭
Who said I'd lied? 'Cause I never, never.
                                      F
Who said I'd lied to her?

Verse 3

          Cm   G/D
And so I drank one it be - came four,
                            E♭   F
And when I fell on the floor, I drank more.

Link 3   As Link 1

Bridge

Cm   G/D
Stop me, oh, oh, oh, stop me,

E♭   F
Stop me if you think that you've heard this one before.

Cm   G/D
Stop me, oh, I said stop me,

E♭   F
Stop me if you think that you've heard this one before.

Cm   G/D
'Cause nothing's changed,

       E♭   F
I still love you, oh I still love you,

    Cm   G/D E♭   F
Only slightly, only slightly less than I used to, my love.

Outro

 ‖: Cm   G/D   E♭
   Set me free, why don't you babe?

         F   Cm
Get out my life, why don't you?

         G/D
'Cause you don't really love me, no,

    E♭   F
You just keep me hanging on. :‖

‖: Cm | G/D | E♭ | F   :‖ *Play 4 times*

| Cm   ‖

You Can't Have It All

Words & Music by
Tim Wheeler

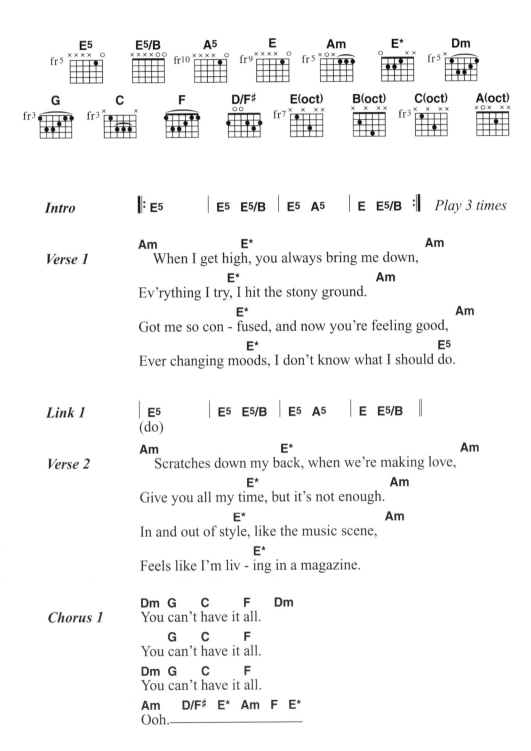

Intro   ‖: E5 | E5 E5/B | E5 A5 | E E5/B :‖   *Play 3 times*

Verse 1

    Am   E*   Am
When I get high, you always bring me down,
              E*   Am
Ev'rything I try, I hit the stony ground.
           E*   Am
Got me so con - fused, and now you're feeling good,
             E*   E5
Ever changing moods, I don't know what I should do.

Link 1 | E5 | E5 E5/B | E5 A5 | E E5/B ‖
(do)

Verse 2

    Am   E*   Am
Scratches down my back, when we're making love,
            E*   Am
Give you all my time, but it's not enough.
           E*   Am
In and out of style, like the music scene,
           E*
Feels like I'm liv - ing in a magazine.

Chorus 1

Dm G   C   F   Dm
You can't have it all.
    G   C   F
You can't have it all.
Dm G   C   F
You can't have it all.
Am   D/F♯ E* Am F E*
Ooh.⎯⎯⎯⎯⎯⎯⎯⎯⎯⎯

Verse 3

Am   E*   Am
  Voices in your head, always doubting me,

                  E*   Am
Paranoid distor - tions of reality.

                     E*   Am
You tell me all the time that there's something wrong,

                  E*
But you never know what you really want.

Chorus 2

Dm G   C   F   Dm
You can't have it all.

     G   C   F
You can't have it all.

Dm G   C   F   Dm
You can't have it all.

     G   C   F   Am D/F# E*
You can't have it, you can't have it all.————

     Am F E*
Ooh.————

Interlude   ‖: E(oct) B(oct) | C(oct) A(oct) | E* F G | E* F G   :‖

Bridge

Dm G   C   F   Dm
You can't have it all.

     G   C   F
You can't have it all.

Link 2 | E5 | E5 E5/B | E5 A5 | E E5/B ‖

Verse 4

Am   E*   Am
  I'm losing my mind, it comes too easily,

                  E*   Am
Blaming someone else, for your misery.

                    E*   N.C.
Walking on eggshells, until you're feeling bad,

                  E*   Dm
This psycho drone is taking over my life.

Chorus 3

Dm G   C   F   Dm
You can't have it all.

     G   C   F
You can't have it all.

Dm G   C   F   Dm
You can't have it all.

     G   C   F   Dm
You can't have it, you can't have it all.

     G   C   F   Dm
You can't have it all. (You can't have it all.)

     G   C   F   Dm
You can't have it all. (You can't have it all.)

      G   C   F   Dm   G   C
(You can't have it all.)   (You can't have it.)

F   Am D/F♯ E*
 You can't have it all._____

You Know My Name

Words & Music by
David Arnold & Chris Cornell

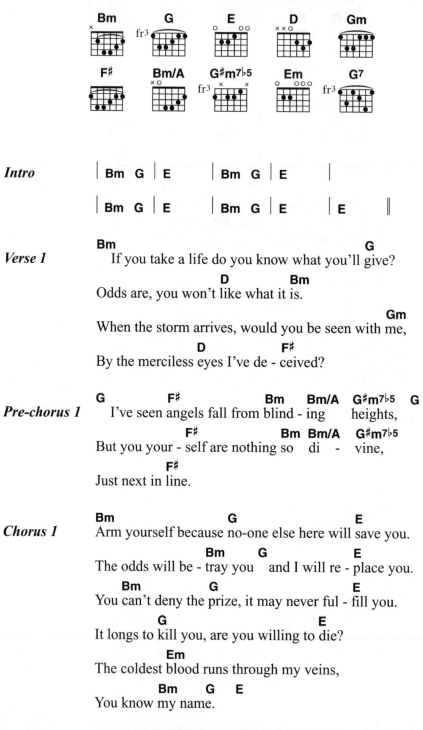

Intro | Bm G | E | Bm G | E |

| Bm G | E | Bm G | E | E ||

Verse 1

Bm
   If you take a life do you know what you'll give? **G**

         D   **Bm**
Odds are, you won't like what it is.

                           Gm
When the storm arrives, would you be seen with me,

         D   **F♯**
By the merciless eyes I've de - ceived?

Pre-chorus 1

G   **F♯**   **Bm** **Bm/A** **G♯m7♭5** **G**
I've seen angels fall from blind - ing   heights,

             F♯   **Bm** **Bm/A** **G♯m7♭5**
But you your - self are nothing so   di -   vine,

           F♯
Just next in line.

Chorus 1

Bm   **G**   **E**
Arm yourself because no-one else here will save you.

            Bm   **G**   **E**
The odds will be - tray you   and I will re - place you.

Bm   **G**   **E**
You can't deny the prize, it may never ful - fill you.

       G   **E**
It longs to kill you, are you willing to die?

      Em
The coldest blood runs through my veins,

      Bm   **G** **E**
You know my name.

Verse 2

Bm   G
   If you come inside things will not be the same
     D   Bm
When you re - turn to the night.
                                Gm
If you think you've won, you never saw me change
             D   F♯
The game that we have been playing.

Pre-chorus 2

G   F♯   Bm   Bm/A Gm7♭5 G
I've seen diamonds cut through hard - er   men,
               F♯   Bm Bm/A   Gm7♭5
Than you your - self, but if you must pre - tend,
                    F♯
You may meet your end.

Chorus 2

Bm   G   E
Arm yourself because no-one else here will save you.
                  Bm   G   E
The odds will be - tray you   and I will re - place you.
         Bm   G   E
You can't deny the prize, it may never ful - fill you.
             G   E
It longs to kill you, are you willing to die?
             Em
The coldest blood runs through my veins...

Bridge

G   E
Try to hide your hand, for - get how to feel (forget how to feel).
G   E
Life is gone with just a spin of the wheel (spin of the wheel).

Chorus 3

Bm   G   E
Arm yourself because no-one else here will save you.
                  Bm   G   E
The odds will be - tray you   and I will re - place you.
         Bm   G   E
You can't deny the prize, it may never ful - fill you.
             G   E
It longs to kill you, are you willing to die?
             Em
The coldest blood runs through my veins,

Outro

                  Bm   G   E
‖: You know my name,   (You know my name). :‖ *Play 3 times*
              Bm   G E
You know my name.

Your Love Alone Is Not Enough

Words & Music by
James Dean Bradfield, Nicky Wire & Sean Moore

Verse 1

    D   A   Em   D   A   Em
Your love a - lone is not e - nough, not e - nough, not e - nough.

    D   A   Em   D
When times get tough, oh, they get tough,

          A   Em
They get tough, they get tough.

    G   D   A   Em
Trade all your heroes in for ghosts, in for ghosts, in for ghosts.

    G   D
They're always the ones who love you most,

          A   Em   D A Em
Love you most, love you most.

Verse 2

    D   A   Em   D   A   Em
Your love a - lone is not e - nough, not e - nough, not e - nough.

    D A   Em   D   A   Em
It's what you felt, it's what you said, what you said, what you said.

    G   D   A   Em
You said the sky would fall on you, fall on you, fall on you.

    G   D
Through all the pain your eyes stayed blue,

          A   Em   D A Em
They stayed blue, baby blue.

Link

| N.C. ‖

Bridge 1

    A   Em   G
But your love alone won't save the world,

                                D   A
You knew the secret of the uni - verse.

                          Em   G
Despite it all you made it worse,

It left you lonely it left you cursed.

Verse 3

    D   **A**   **Em**   **D**
You stole the sun straight from my heart,

        A   **Em**
From my heart, from my heart.

    D   **A**   **Em**   **D**   **A**   **Em**
With no ex - cuses, just fell a - part, fell a - part, fell a - part.

    G   **D**   **A**   **Em**
No you won't make a mess of me, mess of me, mess of me.

    G   **D**
For you're as blind as a man can be,

        A   **Em**   **D** **A** **Em**
Man can be, man can be.

| **N.C.** ‖

Bridge 2

A   **Em**   **G**
I could have seen for miles and miles,

                    D   **A**
I could have made you feel a - live.

                    Em
I could have placed us in e - xile,

                    G
I could have written all your lines.

I could have shown you,

                         D **A** **Em**
I could have shown you how to cry.

Interlude

(Em)   **D** **A** **Em**   **D** **A** **Em**
Your love alone   is not enough,

                  D **A** **Em**   **N.C.**
Your love alone   is not enough.

Instrumental | **A** | **A** | **Em** | **Em** |

                     | **G** | **A** | **D** | **D**   ‖

Bridge 3

A   **Em** **G**
La, la, la, la, la, la, la, la.

                                     D **A** **Em**
I could have shown you, shown you how to cry.

Outro

(Em)   **D** **A** **Em**   **D** **A** **Em**
Your love alone   is not enough,

                  D **A** **Em**
Your love alone.

Your Touch

Words & Music by
Daniel Auerbach & Patrick Carney

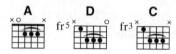

Intro

| N.C. (A) | N.C. (D) N.C. (C) | N.C. (A) | N.C. (D) N.C. (C) ‖

‖: A | D C | A | D C :‖

Verse 1

   A   D C A   D C A
   You're my woman,   and you got it.

          D   C   A   D C
So much,   I'm crazy for it.

Chorus 1

 (C) A   D C   A   D C
Your touch,   your touch.

         A   D C   A   D C
Your touch,   your touch.

Verse 2

   A   D C A   D C A
   Yeah and I'll be good   like I should.

                 D C A   D C
Waiting inside   misery I need...

Chorus 2

As Chorus 1

Interlude

‖: A | D C | A | D C :‖

| N.C. (A) | N.C. (D) N.C. (C) | N.C. (A) | N.C. (D) N.C. (C) ‖

| A | D C | A | D C ‖

Verse 3

   A   D C   A   D C A
Ooh Lordy lord...   I got us out and I,

              D C A   D
Flee the rush,   I need..

Chorus 3

 C A   D C   A   D C
Your touch,   your touch.

         A   D C   A   D C A
Your touch,   your touch.

1 2 3 4 5 6 7 8 9